# The Pocket
# Price Guide
# to
# Goss Models

MILESTONE
PUBLICATIONS

Nicholas Pine

Published and distributed by
Milestone Publications,
Goss & Crested China Ltd.,
62 Murray Road, Horndean, Waterlooville,
Hampshire, PO8 9JL
Telephone Horndean (0705) 597440

Typeset by I.D.S.Ltd., Bishops Waltham, Hampshire
Printed and bound in Great Britain by
Banana House, Goldsmith Avenue, Portsmouth, Hants. PO4 0BT
Tel: (0705) 825883   Fax: (0705) 812754

British Library Cataloguing in Publication Data
A record of this title is available from the British Library

ISBN 1-85265-125-3

# CONTENTS

# BUILDINGS

*Top row*        Grinlow Tower, Windleshaw Chantry, Herne Bay Reculver
                 Towers, Windsor Round Tower, Old Gateway Monnow Bridge.

*Second row*     Tenby Gate, Newcastle Castle, Broadway Tower,
                 Southampton Bargate.

# INTRODUCTION

This pocket size price guide to approximately 700 named models is intended as a quick reference for collectors for use when visiting antique fairs, markets, shops and auctions. On such occasions one no longer need carry the 400+ pages of *The Concise Encyclopaedia and Price Guide to Goss China*, which now weighs approximately 2 lbs. This booklet lists all the historic models and special shapes, cottages and coloured buildings, crosses and fonts produced by the factory during what I have termed the Second Period of manufacture between 1881 and 1934. Pieces that were also produced during the First Period have the symbol [1] after their respective entries.

All items are listed in alphabetical order and refer to the inscriptions found on the base of each model. Prices are given for both models with any arms and for those with matching arms. Correct matching arms are listed in each case. For example, a Seaford Urn bearing the arms of Seaford would be considered matching and sells at a higher price than that of a Seaford Urn bearing any other town arms.

This booklet cannot hope to be a full substitute for the information contained in the main volume but should enable the collector to know quickly and easily, indeed surreptitiously, what to buy and what not to buy.

I have categorised the products of the Goss factory into three periods. The First Period covers ware manufactured by William Henry Goss whilst he owned and ran the factory between 1858 and 1887. The Second Period spans the stewardship of his sons Adolphus, Victor and William Huntley Goss between 1881 and 1934 and the Third Period embraces wares made by other factories but which carry the Goss mark and relates to 1930-1939. It should be noted that values indicated in this guide are for shapes only and do not take into account the value of any arms or decorations. Exceptions to this are the League models bearing correct arms. For all other additional crest and decoration values, the companion volume to this guide, *The Price Guide to Arms and Decorations on Goss China*, by the same author, lists and values some 10,000 different decorations to be found on Goss porcelain.

Prices quoted in this guide are for pieces in perfect condition. Worn gilding, faded coats of arms, chips, cracks and bad firing flaws will all affect value substantially. A small crack could easily halve the value, whilst a cottage worth £100 would probably only be worth £15 with a chimney missing.

Although it is always possible to get a damaged piece restored, it is easy to detect restoration. Where the value of a restored item would be greater than that of the same piece in a damaged state, restoration is worthwhile. However, inexpensive, sub-standard pieces have always been popular, thus making it possible for those with limited resources to obtain a rarer specimen. Indeed, damaged Goss has risen in price proportionally more than perfect Goss in recent years.

Prices herein are drawn from twenty years of experience in buying and selling Goss china. During this period, the author has also made an orderly market in this ware and diligently researched the subject. Prices quoted exclude VAT.

The leading forum for buying and selling is *Goss & Crested China*, a 36 page illustrated monthly catalogue published by Goss and Crested China Ltd. See the final pages in this book for further details. Each edition contains examples of pieces from every period of the factory and is available by annual subscription. The leading club for collectors is The Goss and Crested China Club which publishes a monthly catalogue, holds regular open days, values pieces, answers collectors queries and provides many other services. See the final pages in this book for further details.

The largest stock available for sale in the world is held at the Goss and Crested China Centre, 62 Murray Road, Horndean, Waterlooville, Hampshire, PO8 9JL where thousands of pieces are available for sale in a re-creation of an Edwardian china stall, one such as you might have found on the end of the pier in 1900.

Goss and Crested China Ltd. are always interested in acquiring Goss and crested china. You are invited to write or telephone with details of any pieces which may be available in order to receive our immediate offer.

# Models and Historic Shapes

Models which bear no arms are included in the first column and are marked thus †.
Models from the first period are marked thus [1].
Models from the third period are marked thus [3].
All dimensions refer to the height unless otherwise stated.
Where no price is given, no piece exists in that particular category

| Model | | | With any Arms £ p | With Matching Arms £ p |
|---|---|---|---|---|
| **ABERDEEN BRONZE POT** | | 63mm | 9.00 | 26.00 |
| Matching Arms: *ABERDEEN* | | 89mm | 23.00 | 30.00 |
| Variation with unusually short legs attached to the large size pot, multi crested | | 133mm | 34.50 | 45.00 |
| **ABERGAVENNY ANCIENT JAR** | | 54mm | 7.50 | 22.50 |
| Matching Arms: *ABERGAVENNY* | | | | |
| **ABINGDON ROMAN VASE** | | 95mm | 28.00 | 40.00 |
| Matching Arms: *ABINGDON* | | | | |
| **ACANTHUS ROSE BOWL** | with wire cage | 130mm | 95.00 | |
| This model was originally sold with a wire cage which is often missing nowadays. It has no correct arms. | without wire cage | 130mm | 75.00 | |
| **ALDERNEY FISH BASKET** | | 40mm | | 65.00 |
| Matching Arms: *ALDERNEY* | | 58mm | | 75.00 |
| **ALDERNEY MILK CAN and lid** | | 70mm | | 56.50 |
| This model is incomplete without its lid value £10.00 | | 108mm | | 56.50 |
| Matching Arms: *ALDERNEY* | | 140mm | | 65.00 |
| **ALNWICK CELTIC SEPULCHRAL URN** | | 68mm[1] | 19.00 | 35.00 |
| Matching Arms: *ALNWICK* | | | | |
| **AMERSHAM LEADEN MEASURE** | | 48mm | 13.00 | 43.00 |
| Matching Arms: *AMERSHAM* | | | | |
| **ANTWERP OOLEN POT** | (a) 1 coat of arms | 70mm | 7.50 | 29.00 |
| Matching Arms: *ANTWERPEN* | (b) 3 coats of arms | 70mm | 16.50 | 35.00 |
| **APPLEBY ELIZABETHAN BUSHEL MEASURE** | | | | |
| Matching Arms: *APPLEBY* | | Dia. 59mm | 21.00 | 35.00 |
| **ARUNDEL ROMAN EWER** | | 55mm | 14.50 | 25.00 |
| Matching Arms: *ARUNDEL* | | 102mm | 30.00 | 47.00 |

| Model | | With any Arms £  p | With Matching Arms £  p |
|---|---|---|---|
| **ASHBOURNE BUSHEL** <br> Matching Arms: *ASHBOURNE* | Dia. 51mm | 12.50 | 30.00 |
| **ASHLEY RAILS ROMAN URN** <br> Matching Arms: *MANOR OF NEW MILTON,* <br> *CHRISTCHURCH, LYMINGTON* OR *RINGWOOD* | 108mm | 56.50 | 75.00 |
| **AVEBURY CELTIC URN** <br> Matching Arms: *CALNE, MARLBOROUGH* or *DEVISES* | 105mm[1] | 23.00 | 40.00 |
| **(CUP OF) BALLAFLETCHER** <br> Matching Arms: *DOUGLAS, ISLE OF MAN* <br> With *ANY ISLE OF MAN ARMS* | 95mm | 33.50 | 68.00 <br> 47.50 |
| **BARNET STONE** <br> (a) White† <br> (b) Brown† | 172mm <br> 172mm | 110.00 <br> 150.00 | |
| **BARTLOW EWER** <br> Matching Arms: *SAFFRON WALDEN* | 104mm[1] | 38.00 | 60.00 |
| **BATH ANCIENT ROMAN CUP** <br> Matching Arms: *BATH* | 102mm | 95.00 | 145.00 |
| **BATH BRONZE ROMAN EWER** <br> Matching Arms: *BATH* | 120mm[1] | 30.00 | |
| **BATH ROMAN EWER** <br> Matching Arms: *BATH* | 63mm <br> 130mm | 7.00 <br> 21.00 | 22.50 <br> 35.00 |
| **BATH ROMAN JUG** <br> a) With one or two coats of arms <br> b) With three coats of arms <br> Matching Arms: *BATH* | 150mm[1] <br> 150mm[1] | 35.00 <br> 40.00 | 72.50 <br> 85.00 |
| **BATH URN** <br> Matching Arms: *BATH* | 75mm[1] | 30.00 | 47.00 |
| **BEACHY HEAD LIGHTHOUSE** (a) Brown band <br> (b) Black band <br> Matching Arms: *EASTBOURNE* (with or without addition of <br> BEACHY HEAD) | 125mm <br> 125mm | 55.00 <br> 55.00 | 80.00 <br> 80.00 |
| **BECCLES RINGERS JUG** <br> Matching Arms: *ANCIENT SEAL OF BECCLES* | 87mm | 350.00 | 650.00 |
| **BETTWS-Y-COED ANCIENT BRONZE KETTLE** <br> Matching Arms: *BETTWS-Y-COED* | 73mm <br> 114mm | 15.00 <br> 26.00 | 33.50 <br> 38.50 |

| Model | | With any Arms £  p | With Matching Arms £  p |
|---|---|---|---|
| **BIDEFORD ANCIENT MORTAR**<br>Matching Arms: *BIDEFORD* | 42mm | 12.50 | 33.50 |
| **BLACKGANG CANNON**<br>Matching Arms: *BLACKGANG* | Length 95mm | 14.00 | 25.00 |
| **BLACKGANG TOWER, ST. CATHERINE'S HILL**<br>Matching Arms: *BLACKGANG* | 112mm | 30.00 | 45.00 |
| **BLACKPOOL TOWER**<br>Matching Arms: *BLACKPOOL* | 118mm | 34.50 | 64.00 |
| **BOGNOR LOBSTER TRAP**<br>Matching Arms: *BOGNOR* | 51mm | | 75.00 |
| **BOLTON ABBEY WINE COOLER**<br>Matching Arms: *BOLTON ABBEY* | Dia. 68mm | 23.00 | 40.00 |
| **BOSTON ANCIENT EWER**<br>Matching Arms: *BOSTON* | 70mm | 15.50 | 40.00 |
| **BOULOGNE MILK CAN and lid**<br>The model is incomplete without its lid, value £10.00<br>Matching Arms: *BOULOGNE-SUR-MER* | 74mm | 25.00 | 45.00 |
| **BOULOGNE SEDAN CHAIR**<br>Matching Arms: *BOULOGNE-SUR-MER*<br>One example has been seen by the author decorated in turquoise blue (b). | (a) 69mm<br>(b) 69mm | 40.00<br>350.00 | 65.00 |
| **BOULOGNE WOODEN SHOE**<br>Matching Arms: *BOULOGNE-SUR-MER* | Length 118mm | 34.00 | 80.00 |
| **BOURNEMOUTH ANCIENT BRONZE MACE HEAD**<br>Matching Arms: *BOURNEMOUTH* | 80mm | 27.50 | 37.50 |
| **BOURNEMOUTH ANCIENT EGYPTIAN LAMP**<br>Matching Arms: *BOURNEMOUTH*<br>With Egyptian Arms add £10.00 | Length 105mm | 23.00 | 35.00 |
| **BOURNEMOUTH PILGRIM BOTTLE**<br>Matching Arms: *BOURNEMOUTH* | 90mm | 13.00 | 30.00 |
| **BOURNEMOUTH PINE CONE**<br>Matching Arms: *BOURNEMOUTH* | 90mm | 12.50 | 21.50 |

| Model | | | With any Arms £   p | With Matching Arms £   p |
|---|---|---|---|---|
| **BOURNEMOUTH BRONZE URN** | | 52mm | 13.00 | 25.00 |
| Matching Arms: *BOURNEMOUTH* | | | | |
| **BRADING STOCKS** | | Length 87mm | 155.00 | 285.00 |
| Matching Arms: *THE KING'S TOWN OF BRADING, SEAL OF BRADING* OR *ANCIENT ARMS OF BRADING* | | | | |
| **BRADING ROMAN EWER** | (a) | 70mm | 9.00 | 23.00 |
| Either *THE KING'S TOWN OF BRADING,* | (b) | 125mm[1] | 17.00 | 26.00 |
| *SEAL OF BRADING* OR *ANCIENT ARMS OF BRADING* OR *ISLE OF WIGHT* may be considered as Matching Arms. | | | | |
| **BRAUNTON LIGHTHOUSE** | | 133mm | 600.00 | 750.00 |
| Matching Arms: *WESTWARD HO.* | | | | |
| **(THE NOSE OF) BRASENOSE** | | 104mm | 27.50 | 38.50 |
| The Matching Arms are *BRAZENOSE* OR *ARMS OF THE CITY OF OXFORD.* | | | | |
| **(THE NOSE OF) BRASENOSE** | | 98mm | 65.00 | |
| Second variety with a flat back and pointed nose. | | | | |
| **BRIDLINGTON ELIZABETHAN QUART MEASURE** | | 50mm | 14.00 | 27.50 |
| Matching Arms: *BRIDLINGTON* | | | | |
| **BRISTOL PUZZLE CIDER CUP** | | 51mm | 26.00 | 43.50 |
| Matching Arms: *CITY OF BRISTOL* | | | | |
| **BRITISH (SIX INCH) SHELL** | | 110mm | 25.00 | |
| The value of any military crest is to be added to the price, say £20.00-£60.00 depending upon rarity and suitability. Correct Arms: *ANY ARTILLERY REGIMENT* | | | | |
| **BRITISH TANK** | | Length 110mm | 56.50 | |
| Two versions can be found, with sponson guns pointing upwards, the other with these guns pointing horizontally ahead. Both are of the same value. | | | | |
| Matching Arms: *(a)  LINCOLN* | | | | 75.00 |
| *(b)  TANK CORPS* | | | | 80.00 |
| **BRIXWORTH ANCIENT CUP** | | 55mm | 11.00 | 17.00 |
| Matching Arms: *NORTHAMPTON (SHIRE)* | | | | |

| Model | | | With any Arms £  p | With Matching Arms £  p |
|---|---|---|---|---|
| **BROADWAY TOWER** | (a) White | 75mm | 110.00 | 190.00 |
| Matching Arms: *BROADWAY* | (b) Grey† | 75mm | 195.00 | |
| | (c) Brown† | 75mm | 250.00 | |
| **BURTON BEER BARREL** | | 60mm | 9.50 | 22.50 |
| Matching Arms: *BURTON UPON TRENT* | | 73mm | 19.00 | 28.00 |
| **BURY ST. EDMUNDS GERMAN BOMB** | | 75mm | 28.00 | 43.50 |
| This model has an extremely delicate handle, without which it is of little value. | | | | |
| Matching Arms: *BURY ST. EDMUNDS* | | | | |
| **BURY ST. EDMUNDS KETTLE and lid** | | 76mm | 21.50 | 40.00 |
| This model is not complete without its lid, worth £10.00 of the price shown. | | 121mm[1] | 35.00 | 64.00 |
| Matching Arms: *BURY ST. EDMUNDS* | | | | |
| **CAERHUN ROMAN BURIAL URN** | | 54mm | 21.50 | 40.00 |
| Matching Arms: *CONWAY* | | | | |
| **CAERLEON GLASS LACHRYMATORY (or Tear Bottle)** | | 86mm | 10.00 | |
| Matching Arms: *(a) CAERLEON* | | | | 30.00 |
| *(b) NEWPORT* | | | | 26.00 |
| **CAERLEON LAMP** | | | | |
| Matching Arms: *(a) CAERLEON* | | Length 88mm | 10.00 | 26.00 |
| *(b) NEWPORT* | | | | 19.50 |
| **CAMBRIDGE PITCHER** | | 63mm | 7.00 | 22.50 |
| Matching Arms: *CAMBRIDGE* | | 108mm | 14.50 | 23.00 |
| **CAMBRIDGE ROMAN JUG** | | 70mm | 17.50 | 26.00 |
| Matching Arms: *CAMBRIDGE* | | 76mm | 17.50 | 26.00 |
| | | 82mm | 17.50 | 26.00 |
| | | 88mm | 25.00 | 38.00 |
| | | 94mm | 30.00 | 47.00 |
| | | 120mm | 30.00 | 47.00 |
| | | 130mm | 32.50 | 50.00 |
| | | 140mm | 40.00 | 55.00 |
| | | 155mm | 50.00 | 60.00 |
| **CANARY PORRON** | | 68mm | 24.50 | 40.00 |
| Matching Arms: *LAS PALMAS, GRAND CANARY* | | | | |
| **CANTERBURY JUG** | | 113mm[1] | 19.00 | 28.00 |
| Matching Arms: *CANTERBURY* | | | | |

| Model | | | With any Arms £   p | With Matching Arms £   p |
|---|---|---|---|---|
| **CANTERBURY LEATHER BOTTLE**<br>Matching Arms: *CANTERBURY* | | 46mm | 6.50 | 14.00 |
| **CAPEL MADOC STOUP**<br>Matching Arms: *RHAYADER* | | Length 80mm | 28.00 | 65.00 |
| **CARDINAL BEAUFORT'S CANDLESTICK**<br>Matching Arms: *CARDINAL BEAUFORT* OR<br> *WINCHESTER* | | 152mm[1] | 110.00 | 225.00 |
| **CARDINAL BEAUFORT'S SALT CELLAR**<br>MAtching Arms: *CARDINAL BEAUFORT* OR<br>*WINCHESTER* | | 70mm[1] | 65.00 | 125.00 |
| **CARLISLE OLD SALT POT**<br>Matching Arms: *CARLISLE* | | 46mm | 6.50 | 17.00 |
| **CARMARTHEN CORACLE**<br>Matching Arms: *CARMARTHEN* | | Length 133mm[1] | 72.50 | 115.00 |
| **CARNARVON EWER**<br>Matching Arms: *CARNARVON* | | 63mm<br>89mm[1] | 8.50<br>14.50 | 22.50<br>30.00 |
| **CASTLETOWN CINERARY URN**<br>Matching Arms: *CASTLETOWN, ISLE OF MAN* | | 40mm | 14.50 | 26.00 |
| **CENOTAPH, WHITEHALL**<br>Matching Arms: *CITY OF LONDON* OR *WESTMINSTER* OR *CITY OF*<br>*WESTMINSTER* | (a) White glazed<br>(b) White unglazed† | 145mm<br>145mm | 30.00<br>47.50 | 42.00 |
| **CHEDDAR CHEESE**<br>Matching Arms: *CHEDDAR* | (a) Yellow<br>(b) White glazed [3] | 62mm<br>62mm | 33.50†<br>22.50 | 47.50<br>47.50 |
| **CHERBOURG MILK CAN and lid**<br>This model is not complete without its lid which is<br>worth £12.00 of the price shown.<br>Matching Arms: *CHERBOURG* | | 65mm | 25.00 | 65.00 |
| **CHESHIRE SALT BLOCK**<br>Matching Arms: *CHESHIRE* | | 80mm | 31.00 | 42.00 |
| **CHESTER ROMAN VASE**<br>Matching Arms: *CHESTER* | | 59mm<br>89mm[1] | 6.50<br>16.00 | 14.50<br>28.00 |
| **CHESTERFIELD BRAMPTON WARE MUG**<br>Matching Arms: *CHESTERFIELD* | | 93mm | 40.00 | 65.00 |

| Model | | | With any Arms £ p | With Matching Arms £ p |
|---|---|---|---|---|
| **CHICHESTER ROMAN EWER** Matching Arms: *CHICHESTER* | | 63mm | 6.50 | 15.50 |
| **CHICHESTER ROMAN URN** Matching Arms: *CHICHESTER* | | 81mm[1] | 17.50 | 30.00 |
| **CHICKEN ROCK LIGHTHOUSE** Matching Arms: *ISLE OF MAN* | | 127mm | 34.50 | 47.50 |
| **CHILE HAT** Matching Arms: *CHILE* | | Dia. 86mm | 215.00 | 385.00 |
| **CHILE MATE CUP** Matching Arms: *CHILE* | | 60mm | 100.00 | 175.00 |
| **CHILE SPUR** Matching Arms: *CHILE* | | Length 150mm | 200.00 | 300.00 |
| **CHILE STIRRUP** Matching Arms: *CHILE* | | 50mm | 100.00 | 175.00 |
| **CHRISTCHURCH ANCIENT BOWL** Matching Arms: *CHRISTCHURCH* | | Dia. 60mm | 10.50 | 26.00 |
| **CHRISTCHURCH PRIORY CHURCH NORMAN TOWER** | (a) White glazed† | 123mm | 56.50 | |
| | (b) White unglazed† | 123mm | 80.00 | |
| | (c) Grey† | 123mm | 82.50 | |
| | (d) Brown† | 123mm | 155.00 | |
| **CHRISTCHURCH ROMANO-BRITISH URN** Matching Arms: *CHRISTCHURCH* | | 52mm | 9.00 | 25.00 |
| **CIRENCESTER ROMAN EWER** Matching Arms: *CIRENCESTER* | (a) 1 Arms | 115mm [1] | 32.50 | 46.50 |
| | (b) 2 Arms | 115mm[1] | 40.00 | 60.00 |
| | (c) 3 Arms | 115mm [1] | 47.50 | 65.00 |
| **CIRENCESTER ROMAN URN** This model often appears in coloured lustre glaze and uncrested Matching Arms: *CIRENCESTER* | | 165mm | 87.00 | 130.00 |
| **CIRENCESTER ROMAN VASE** Matching Arms: *CIRENCESTER* | | 80mm | 10.50 | 24.50 |
| | | 124mm | 17.50 | 30.00 |

| Model | | | With any Arms £ p | With Matching Arms £ p |
|---|---|---|---|---|
| **CLIFTONVILLE ROMAN JUG** | | 180mm | 175.00 | 220.00 |
| Matching Arms: *MARGATE* | | | | |
| | | | | |
| **CLIFTONVILLE ROMAN VASE** | | 70mm | 195.00 | 265.00 |
| Matching Arms: *MARGATE* | | 107mm | 195.00 | 265.00 |
| | | | | |
| **COLCHESTER GIGANTIC ROMAN WINE VASE** | | 157mm | 56.50 | 95.00 |
| Matching Arms: *COLCHESTER* | | | | |
| | a) With one coat of arms | | | |
| | b) With four coats of arms | | 65.00 | 115.00 |
| | | | | |
| **COLCHESTER NATIVE OYSTER SHELL** | | Width 68mm | 12.50 | 21.50 |
| Always appears unnamed. | | | | |
| Matching Arms: *COLCHESTER AND CINQUE PORT LIBERTY OF BRIGHTLINGSEA* | | | | |
| | | | | |
| **COLCHESTER VASE (Cloaca)** | | | | |
| Correct Arms: | a) With one coat of arms | 45mm | 7.50 | 21.50 |
| *COLCHESTER* | b) With three coats of arms | 45mm | 12.50 | 29.50 |
| | | | | |
| **COLCHESTER ROMAN VASE (Famous)** | | 44mm | 6.50 | 17.00 |
| Matching Arms: *COLCHESTER* | | 90mm | 20.00 | 30.00 |
| | a) With one coat of arms | 127mm | 26.00 | 35.00 |
| | b) With four coats of arms | 127mm | 35.00 | 45.00 |
| | | | | |
| **CORFE CASTLE CUP** | | 62mm[1] | 15.50 | 27.50 |
| Matching Arms: *CORFE CASTLE* | | | | |
| | | | | |
| **CORNISH BUSSA** | | 55mm | 8.50 | 19.50 |
| Matching Arms: *CORNWALL* | | | | |
| | | | | |
| **CORNISH PASTY** | | | | |
| Matching Arms: *CORNWALL* | | Length | | |
| | (a) White glazed | 82mm | 47.50 | 75.00 |
| | (b) Yellow | 82mm | 70.00 | 110.00 |
| | (c) White glazed | 87mm | 47.50 | 75.00 |
| | (d) White glazed | 110mm | 60.00 | 82.50 |
| | (e) Yellow | 110mm | 82.50 | 117.50 |
| | | | | |
| **CORNISH STILE** | (a) White unglazed† | Length | 95.00 | |
| | (b) White glazed† | 72mm | 52.50 | |
| | (c) Brown† | | 95.00 | |
| Variety (b) can be found with the Blackpool arms, which would reduce its value by half. | | | | |
| | | | | |
| **CUCKFIELD ANCIENT BELLARMINE** | | 75mm | 16.00 | 25.00 |
| Matching Arms: *CUCKFIELD* | | | | |

| Model | | | With any Arms £ p | With Matching Arms £ p |
|---|---|---|---|---|

### CUMBRAE, THE MONUMENT, TOMONT END

| | | Brown† 175mm | 375.00 | |
|---|---|---|---|---|

**DARTMOUTH SACK BOTTLE**
Matching Arms: *DARTMOUTH*
When matching arms are shown without a shield, as a
pictorial presentation: Add £10.00

| | | 63mm | 10.00 | 20.00 |
|---|---|---|---|---|
| | | 92mm[1] | 16.50 | 22.50 |

**DENBIGH BRICK**
Matching Arms: *DENBIGH*

| | (a) White glazed | 82mm[1] | 75.00 | 87.50 |
|---|---|---|---|---|
| | (b) White unglazed† | 82mm | 87.50 | |
| | (c) Brown or red† | 82mm | 265.00 | |

**DEVIZES CELTIC DRINKING CUP**
Matching Arms: *DEVIZES*

| | | 63mm | 10.50 | 25.00 |
|---|---|---|---|---|
| | | 82mm | 19.00 | 28.00 |

**DEVON CIDER BARREL**
Matching Arms: *DEVON* OR *ANY DEVONSHIRE ARMS*

| | | 60mm | 15.00 | 30.00 |
|---|---|---|---|---|

**DEVON COOKING POT**
Matching Arms: *DEVON* OR *ANY DEVONSHIRE ARMS*

| | | 46mm | 15.00 | 30.00 |
|---|---|---|---|---|

**DEVON OAK PITCHER**
Matching Arms: *DEVON* OR *ANY DEVONSHIRE ARMS*

| | | 59mm | 6.50 | 17.50 |
|---|---|---|---|---|
| | | 114mm[1] | 17.00 | 33.00 |

**DINANT WOODEN SHOE**
Matching Arms: *DINANT*

| | | Length 74mm | 25.00 | 47.50 |
|---|---|---|---|---|

**DONCASTER EWER**
Matching Arms: *DONCASTER*

| | | 67mm | 17.50 | 42.50 |
|---|---|---|---|---|

**DONCASTER URN**
Matching Arms: *DONCASTER*

| | | 39mm | 12.00 | 36.00 |
|---|---|---|---|---|

**DONCASTER VASE**
Matching Arms: *DONCASTER*

| | | 78mm | 17.50 | 42.50 |
|---|---|---|---|---|

**DORCHESTER JUG**
Matching Arms: *DORCHESTER*

| | | 50mm | 6.50 | 17.00 |
|---|---|---|---|---|

**DORCHESTER ROMAN CUP**
Matching Arms: *DORCHESTER*

| | | 51mm | 7.00 | 20.00 |
|---|---|---|---|---|
| | | 82mm[1] | 21.50 | 30.00 |

**DOROTHY VERNON'S PORRIDGE POT**
Matching Arms: *DOROTHY VERNON*

| | | 72mm[1] | 19.00 | 30.00 |
|---|---|---|---|---|

| Model | | With any Arms £   p | With Matching Arms £   p |
|---|---|---|---|
| **DOVER MORTAR (or Stone Vessel)** | 51mm | 8.50 | 17.00 |
| Matching Arms: *DOVER* | | | |
| **DUNGENESS LIGHTHOUSE** | 125mm | | 450.00 |
| Matching Arms: *THE LORDS OF THE LEVEL OF ROMNEY MARSH* | | | |

**DURHAM SANCTUARY KNOCKER**

| | | | |
|---|---|---|---|
| (a) Flower holder, or hair tidy, white glazed | Height 125mm | 40.00† | |
| (b) Flower holder, or hair tidy, white unglazed | Height 125mm | 40.00† | |
| (c) Flower holder, or hair tidy, brown | Height 125mm | 49.00† | |
| (d) Flower holder, or hair tidy, gold front on brown. Probably an 1887 Golden Jubilee Edition. | Height 125mm | 100.00† | |
| (e) Flower holder, or hair tidy, brown with green tingeing | 125mm | 115.00† | |
| (f) Night-light with base | 83mm | 95.00 | 117.50 |
| (g) Mug or cup | 52mm | 40.00 | 65.00 |
| (h) Mug or cup | 80mm | 56.50 | 82.50 |
| (i) Mug or cup | 118mm | 82.50 | 110.00 |

Matching Arms: *DURHAM (CATHEDRAL)*

| | | | |
|---|---|---|---|
| **DUTCH SABOT** | Length 82mm | 19.50 | 40.00 |
| Matching Arms: *HOLLAND* OR *ANY DUTCH TOWN* | | | |
| **DUTCH MILK CAN and lid** (identical to Boulogne Milk Can) This model is incomplete without its lid, value £10.00 | 74mm | 65.00 | 95.00 |
| Matching Arms: *HOLLAND* OR *ANY DUTCH TOWN* | | | |
| **EDDYSTONE LIGHTHOUSE** Matching Arms: *PLYMOUTH, DEVONPORT* OR *STONEHOUSE* | 125mm | 26.00 | 40.00 |
| **EGYPTIAN WATER JAR** | 56mm | 7.00 | 40.00 |
| Matching Arms: *EGYPT* OR *ANY EGYPTIAN ARMS* | | | |
| **EGYPTIAN CANOPIC JAR WITH ANUBIS HEAD No.1** The model is incomplete without its lid, which is worth £40.00. | 76mm | 95.00 | 117.50 |
| Matching Arms: *EGYPT* OR *ANY EGYPTIAN ARMS* | | | |
| **EGYPTIAN KOHL POT No. 4** | 66mm | 30.00 | 65.00 |
| Matching Arms: *EGYPT* OR *ANY EGYPTIAN ARMS* | | | |
| **EGYPTIAN KOHL POT No. 5** | 60mm | 25.00 | 47.50 |
| Matching Arms: *EGYPT* OR *ANY EGYPTIAN ARMS* | | | |

| Model | | | With any Arms £ p | With Matching Arms £ p |
|---|---|---|---|---|
| **EGYPTIAN KOHL POT No. 6** | Dia. 70mm | | 19.50 | 65.00 |
| Matching Arms: *EGYPT* OR *ANY EGYPTIAN ARMS* | | | | |
| **EGYPTIAN ALABASTER VASE No. 7** | 105mm | | 24.00 | 47.50 |
| Matching Arms: *EGYPT* OR *ANY EGYPTIAN ARMS* | | | | |
| **EGYPTIAN ALABASTER VASE No. 8** | 105mm | | 26.00 | 56.50 |
| Matching Arms: *EGYPT* OR *ANY EGYPTIAN ARMS* | | | | |
| **EGYPTIAN ALABASTER BOWL No. 9** | 58mm | | 16.00 | 56.50 |
| Matching Arms: *EGYPT* OR *ANY EGYPTIAN ARMS* | | | | |
| **EGYPTIAN WOODEN EWER No. 10** | 66mm | | 20.50 | 47.50 |
| Matching Arms: *EGYPT* OR *ANY EGYPTIAN ARMS* | | | | |
| **EGYPTIAN PORCELAIN EWER No. 11** | 58mm | | 21.50 | 47.50 |
| Matching Arms: *EGYPT* OR *ANY EGYPTIAN ARMS* | | | | |
| **EGYPTIAN PORCELAIN BOTTLE No. 16** | 68mm | | 43.00 | 65.00 |
| Matching Arms: *EGYPT* OR *ANY EGYPTIAN ARMS* | | | | |
| **EGYPTIAN MOCHA CUP (Bowl Shaped)** | Named 40mm | | 9.00 | 41.50 |
| Matching Arms: *EGYPT* | Unnamed 40mm | | 6.00 | 40.00 |
| OR *ANY EGYPTIAN ARMS* | | | | |
| **EGYPTIAN MOCHA CUP (Egg Cup Shaped)** | Named 52mm | | 12.50 | 41.50 |
| Matching Arms: *EGYPT* | Unnamed 52mm | | 10.50 | 40.00 |
| OR *ANY EGYPTIAN ARMS* | | | | |
| **ELIZABETHAN JUG** | 95mm[1] | | 30.00 | 43.00 |
| Matching Arms: *QUEEN ELIZABETH* | | | | |
| **ELLESMERE ANCIENT BRITISH CANOE** | | | | |
| Matching Arms: | (a) White glazed | Length 149mm | 56.50 | 100.00 |
| *ELLESMERE* | (b) Brown† | Length 149mm | 220.00 | |
| **ETON VASE** | 86mm | | 10.50 | 21.50 |
| Matching Arms: *FLOREAT ETONA* OR *WINDSOR* | | | | |
| **EXETER FLEMISH GOBLET** | (a) 130mm | | 19.50 | 32.50 |
| Matching Arms: *EXETER* (a) | (b) 130mm | | 35.00 | 56.50 |
| Matching Arms: *ANTWERPEN* OR *PROVINCIE* | | | | |
| *ANTWERPEN (b)* | | | | |
| **EXETER VASE** | 63mm | | 7.00 | 19.00 |
| Matching Arms: *EXETER* | 101mm | | 19.50 | 26.00 |

| Model | | With any Arms £ p | With Matching Arms £ p |
|---|---|---|---|
| **FELIXSTOWE ROMAN EWER** <br> Matching Arms: *FELIXSTOWE* | 73mm <br> 114mm | 8.00 <br> 22.00 | 34.00 <br> 34.00 |
| **FELIXSTOWE ROMAN CINERARY URN** <br> Matching Arms: *FELIXSTOWE* | 47mm | 8.50 | 26.00 |
| **FENNY STRATFORD POPPER** <br> Matching Arms: *FENNY STRATFORD* | 58mm | 15.50 | 35.00 |
| **FISH BASKET** <br> See also Alderney, Guernsey, Jersey, Sark, and Welsh <br> Fish Basket | 63mm | | 26.00 |
| **(OLD) FLEMISH MELK POT** <br> Matching Arms: *ANTWERPEN* | Max. Dia. 118mm | 19.50 | 35.00 |
| **FOLKESTONE SALTWOOD ROMAN EWER** <br> Matching Arms: *FOLKESTONE* OR *HYTHE* | 88mm[1] | 13.00 | 21.50 |
| **FOUNTAINS ABBEY, ABBOT'S CUP** <br> Matching Arms: *FOUNTAINS ABBEY* | 44mm <br> 76mm[1] | 7.00 <br> 14.50 | 16.00 <br> 30.00 |
| **FOURSHIRE STONE** <br> Matching Arms: *CHIPPING NORTON* | 118mm | 35.00 | 76.00 |
| **FRASER (FORT AUGUSTUS) CUACH** <br> Matching Arms: *LORD LOVAT*, who is Head of the Fraser Clan, <br> or other Highland Arms are considered matching. | Length 104mm | 17.50 | 35.00 |
| **FROXFIELD ROMAN BRONZE** <br> **DRINKING BOWL** <br> This model was originally sold without arms and <br> subsequently with those of MARLBOROUGH which are <br> considered matching. | Dia. 72mm | 40.00 | 55.00 |
| **GERMAN SMOKING PIPE** <br> Matching Arms: *FRANCO-BRITISH EXHIBITION 1908* for which <br> it was first made. Also *GERMAN* arms could be considered <br> appropriate. | Overall Length 252mm | 70.00 | 100.00 |
| **GERRANS CELTIC CINERARY URN** <br> Matching Arms: *FALMOUTH* | With 1 coat of arms 57mm <br> With 1 coat of arms 127mm[1] <br> With 3 coats of arms 57mm <br> With 3 coats of arms 127mm[1] | 8.00 <br> 14.00 <br> 15.50 <br> 23.00 | 14.00 <br> 30.00 <br> 23.00 <br> 30.00 |

| Model | | With any Arms £ p | With Matching Arms £ p |
|---|---|---|---|
| **GIBRALTAR ALCARAZA or SPANISH CARAFE** <br> Matching Arms: *GIBRALTAR* OR *SPAIN* | 68mm | 7.00 | 25.00 |
| **GLASTONBURY (ABBOT BEERE'S) JACK** <br> Matching Arms: *ARMS OF GLASTONBURY* | 56mm | 7.00 | 21.50 |
| **GLASTONBURY ANCIENT SALT CELLAR** <br> Matching Arms: *ARMS OF GLASTONBURY* | 82mm | 19.00 | 30.00 |
| **GLASTONBURY BRONZE BOWL** <br> Matching Arms: *ARMS OF GLASTONBURY*   Dia. (overall) 65mm Height 73mm <br> Dia. (overall) 127mm Height 80mm [1] | | 14.00 <br> 40.00 | 26.00 <br> 56.50 |
| **GLASTONBURY ROMAN EWER** <br> Matching Arms: *ARMS OF GLASTONBURY* | 71mm | 7.00 | 20.50 |
| **GLASTONBURY TERRACOTTA BOWL** <br> Matching Arms: *ARMS OF GLASTONBURY* | 36mm | 6.50 | 16.00 |
| **GLASTONBURY VASE** <br> Matching Arms: *ARMS OF GLASTONBURY* | 45mm | 6.50 | 16.00 |
| **GLOUCESTER JUG** <br> Matching Arms: *GLOUCESTER ANCIENT OR MODERN* | 44mm <br> 95mm[1] | 6.50 <br> 19.50 | 15.50 <br> 28.00 |
| **GODALMING ANCIENT EWER** <br> Matching Arms: *GODALMING* | 55mm | 17.00 | 28.00 |
| **GOODWIN SANDS CARAFE** <br> Matching Arms: *BROADSTAIRS, DEAL, MARGATE, RAMSGATE,* OR *WALMER* | 61mm | 6.50 | 12.50 |
| **GRAVESEND ORIENTAL WATER COOLER** <br> Matching Arms: *GRAVESEND* | 72mm | 21.50 | 30.00 |
| **(THE) GREAT PYRAMID** <br> Matching Arms: *EGYPT* OR *ANY EGYPTIAN ARMS,* particularly *SAKKARA* | 60mm | 75.00 | 87.00 |
| **GREENWICH VASE** <br> Matching Arms: *GREENWICH* | 86mm | 30.00 | 47.50 |
| **GRINLOW TOWER** <br> Matching Arms: *BUXTON* | 95mm | 160.00 | 295.00 |
| **GUERNSEY FISH BASKET** <br> Matching Arms: *GUERNSEY* | 45mm <br> 58mm <br> Length 116mm 58mm[1] | 14.50 <br> 29.00 <br> 35.00 | 34.50 <br> 40.00 <br> 90.00 |

| Model | | With any Arms £ p | With Matching Arms £ p |
|---|---|---|---|
| **GUERNSEY MILK CAN and lid** | 70mm | | 23.00 |
| This model is incomplete without its lid, value £10.00. | 108mm | 25.00 | 40.00 |
| Matching Arms: *GUERNSEY* | 130mm | 30.00 | 40.00 |
| **GUILDFORD ROMAN VASE** | 63mm | 16.50 | 24.50 |
| Matching Arms: *GUILDFORD* | | | |
| **GUILLEMOT EGG** (a) Coloured, Open | 83mm | 75.00 | |
| Found closed, or open as (b) Coloured, Closed | 93mm | 75.00 | |
| hanging posy vase either (c) White, unglazed, Closed | 96mm | 82.50 | |
| with or without arms, none of which may be considered matching. It is however preferable to have the arms of a coastal town. | | | |
| **GUY'S PORRIDGE POT** | 50mm | 14.50 | 22.00 |
| Matching Arms: *WARWICK* | | | |
| Can be found inscribed in Gothic script. | | 40.00 | |
| **GUY'S PORRIDGE POT** | 40mm | 70.00 | |
| Inscribed in Gothic Script. | | | |
| The only example seen in this size has the arms of Stratford-on-Avon. | | | |
| **HAAMOGA AMAUI, TONGA** | 82mm | 725.00 | 2125.00 |
| Matching Arms: *TONGA* | Length 106mm | | |
| **HAFOD GREEK VASE and lid** | 82mm | 60.00 | 90.00 |
| Both the lid and the base are worth £30.00 each. | | | |
| Matching Arms: *DEVIL'S BRIDGE* (transfer) | | | |
| **HAMBLEDON CRICKET STONE** | Grey 80mm† | 830.00 | |
| **HAMWORTHY LAMP** | Length 100mm | 11.00 | 21.50 |
| Matching Arms: *POOLE* | Width 65mm | | |
| **HARROGATE ANCIENT EWER** | 62mm | 7.00 | 21.50 |
| Matching Arms: *HARROGATE* | | | |
| **HASTINGS KETTLE** | 51mm | 7.00 | 16.00 |
| Matching Arms: *HASTINGS* | | | |
| **HAWES ANCIENT BRITISH URN** | Dia. 95mm | 18.50 | 40.00 |
| Matching Arms: *HAWES* | | | |
| **HAWKINS HENLEY SCULL** | Length 152mm | 60.00 | 75.00 |
| Matching Arms: *HENLEY-ON-THAMES ANCIENT* OR *HENLEY-ON-THAMES 1624* | | | |
| **HEREFORD TERRACOTTA KETTLE and lid** | 70mm | 22.50 | 40.00 |
| This model is incomplete without its lid, worth £8.00 | 121mm[1] | 38.50 | 57.50 |
| Matching Arms: *HEREFORD* | | | |

| Model | | | | With any Arms £ p | With Matching Arms £ p |
|---|---|---|---|---|---|
| **HERNE BAY RECULVER TOWERS** | | | | | |
| Matching Arms: *HERNE BAY* | (a) White glazed | 101mm | | 82.50 | 140.00 |
| | (b) Grey† | 101mm | | 220.00 | |
| | (c) Brown† | 101mm | | 200.00 | |
| **HERNE BAY ANCIENT EWER** | | | 78mm | 7.00 | 17.00 |
| Matching Arms: *HERNE BAY* | | | | | |
| **HERTFORD ANCIENT EWER** | | | 69mm | 12.50 | 25.00 |
| Matching Arms: *HERTFORD* | | | | | |
| **HEXHAM ABBEY FRID STOL** | (a) White unglazed | 60mm | | 26.00 | 32.50 |
| Matching Arms: *HEXHAM ABBEY* | (b) White glazed | 60mm | | 26.00 | 32.50 |
| | (c) Brown | 60mm | | 40.00 | 56.50 |
| | (d) Brown, two-piece as pin box and lid | 60mm | | 85.00 | 120.00 |
| **HITCHIN POSSET CUP** | | | 51mm | 14.00 | 26.00 |
| Matching Arms: *HITCHIN* | | | | | |
| **HORNSEA ATWICK ROMAN VASE** | | | 51mm | 10.00 | 30.00 |
| Matching Arms: *HORNSEA* | | | | | |
| **(THE OLD) HORSE SHOE** | | | 115mm | 21.50 | |
| It has no matching arms, but those of PORTSMOUTH or ADMIRAL LORD NELSON are preferable. | | | | | |
| **HORSHAM JUG** | | | 60mm | 7.00 | 22.50 |
| Matching Arms: *HORSHAM* | | | | | |
| **HUNSTANTON EWER** | | | 65mm | 7.00 | 26.00 |
| Matching Arms: *HUNSTANTON* | | | | | |
| **HYTHE CROMWELLIAN MORTAR** | | | 38mm | 9.00 | 16.00 |
| Matching Arms: *HYTHE* | | | | | |
| **HYTHE CRYPT SKULL** | (a) Small pale yellow† | 38mm | | 75.00 | |
| | (b) Large white† | 72mm | | 110.00 | |
| | (c) Large pale yellow† | 72mm | | 170.00 | |
| **ILKLEY ROMAN EWER** | | | 60mm | 7.00 | 23.00 |
| Matching Arms: *ILKLEY* | | | 132mm | 21.50 | 29.00 |
| **IPSWICH ANCIENT EWER** | | | 60mm | 7.50 | 18.50 |
| Matching Arms: *IPSWICH* | | | | | |

| Model | | With any Arms £ p | With Matching Arms £ p |
|---|---|---|---|
| **IPSWICH ROMAN EWER** <br> Matching Arms: *IPSWICH* | 98mm | 18.50 | 40.00 |
| **IRISH BRONZE POT** | 43mm | 6.50 | 23.00 |
| | 72mm | 14.50 | 30.00 |
| Matching Arms: *ARMS OF IRELAND* OR *ANY IRISH ARMS* | | | |
| **IRISH MATHER** <br> Matching Arms: *ARMS OF IRELAND* <br> OR *ANY IRISH ARMS* | 76mm | 10.50 | 22.50 |
| | Multi-crested 152mm | 47.50 | 75.00 |
| **IRISH WOODEN NOGGIN** <br> Matching Arms: *ARMS OF IRELAND* OR *ANY IRISH ARMS* | 63mm | 10.50 | 27.50 |
| **ITFORD LEWES URN** <br> Matching Arms: *LEWES* | 66mm | 8.50 | 23.00 |
| | 111mm[1] | 22.50 | 34.50 |
| **JAPAN EWER** <br> Matching Arms: *JAPAN* | 90mm | 12.50 | 40.00 |
| | 200mm[1] | 34.50 | 75.00 |
| **JERSEY FISH BASKET** <br> Matching Arms: *JERSEY* | 45mm | 14.50 | 30.00 |
| | 60mm[1] | 22.50 | 34.50 |
| **JERSEY MILK CAN and lid** <br> This model is incomplete without its lid <br> which is worth £10.00 <br> Matching Arms: *JERSEY* | 70mm | | 23.00 |
| | 108mm | 25.00 | 40.00 |
| | 140mm | 30.00 | 40.00 |
| **KENDAL JUG** <br> Matching Arms: *KENDAL* | 86mm | 14.00 | 34.00 |
| | 145mm[1] | 30.00 | 47.50 |
| **KETTERING URN** <br> Matching Arms: *KETTERING* | 43mm | 6.50 | 25.00 |
| **KING ALFRED'S STATUE** | 170mm | 82.50 | |
| **KING RICHARD'S WELL COVER** <br> Matching Arms: *MARKET BOSWORTH* | 100mm | 155.00 | 240.00 |
| **KININMONTH MOSS ANCIENT POT** <br> Matching Arms: *OLD DEER* | 49mm | 17.00 | 35.00 |
| **LANCASHIRE CLOG** <br> Matching Arms: *LANCASHIRE* | Length 93mm | 47.50 | 65.00 |
| **LANCASTER JUG** <br> Matching Arms: *LANCASTER* | 68mm | 6.50 | 30.00 |

| Model | | | | With any Arms £ p | With Matching Arms £ p |
|---|---|---|---|---|---|
| **LANLAWREN CELTIC SEPULCHRAL URN** | | | 50mm | 6.50 | 17.00 |
| Matching Arms: *FOWEY OR POSSIBLY FALMOUTH* | | | 102mm[1] | 22.00 | 28.00 |
| | | | | | |
| **(BATTLE OF) LARGS MEMORIAL TOWER** | | | | | |
| | (a) | White glazed | 128mm | 37.50 | 47.50 |
| Matching Arms: *LARGS* | (b) | Grey glazed | 128mm | 305.00 | |
| | | | | | |
| **LAS PALMAS ANCIENT COVERED JARRA and lid** | | | 58mm | 14.50 | 34.50 |
| This model is incomplete without its lid, value £6.00 | | | | | |
| Matching Arms: *LAS PALMAS* | | | | | |
| | | | | | |
| **LAS PALMAS ANCIENT EARTHEN JAR** | | | 58mm | 14.00 | 26.00 |
| Matching Arms: *LAS PALMAS* | | | | | |
| | | | | | |
| **LAS PALMAS ANCIENT JARRA** | | | 53mm | 10.50 | 25.00 |
| Matching Arms: *LAS PALMAS* | | | | | |
| | | | | | |
| **LAXEY GRETCH-VEG URN** | | | Dia. 55mm | 12.50 | 22.50 |
| Matching Arms: *LAXEY, ISLE OF MAN.* | | | | | |
| | | | | | |
| **LEEK URN** | | | 63mm | 14.00 | 28.00 |
| Matching Arms: *LEEK* | | | | | |
| | | | | | |
| **LEICESTER TYG** | (a) | 1 coat of arms | 59mm | 8.50 | 21.50 |
| Matching Arms: *LEICESTER* | (b) | 3 coats of arms | 59mm | 19.00 | 30.00 |
| | | | | | |
| **LEISTON ABBEY PITCHER** | | | 61mm | 7.00 | 19.00 |
| Matching Arms: *LEISTON ABBEY* | | | 107mm | 21.50 | 30.00 |
| | | | | | |
| **LETCHWORTH CELTIC CINERARY URN** | | | 97mm | 40.00 | 70.00 |
| Matching Arms: *LETCHWORTH* | | | | | |
| | | | | | |
| **LETCHWORTH ROMAN CARINATED VASE** | | | 60mm | 65.00 | 150.00 |
| Matching Arms: *LETCHWORTH* | | | | | |
| | | | | | |
| **LETCHWORTH ROMAN CINERARY URN** | | | 83mm | 375.00 | 550.00 |
| Matching Arms: *LETCHWORTH* | | | | | |
| | | | | | |
| **LETCHWORTH ROMAN VASE** | | | 86mm | 375.00 | 550.00 |
| Matching Arms: *LETCHWORTH* | | | | | |
| | | | | | |
| **LEWES ROMAN VASE** | | | 35mm[1] | 6.50 | 17.00 |
| Matching Arms: *LEWES* | | | | | |
| | | | | | |
| **LICHFIELD JUG** | | | 60mm | 6.50 | 19.50 |
| Matching Arms: *LICHFIELD* | | | 121mm[1] | 19.50 | 30.00 |

| Model | | | With any Arms £  p | With Matching Arms £  p |
|---|---|---|---|---|
| **LINCOLN LEATHER JACK** | | | | |
| (a) White glazed | | 56mm | 10.50 | 22.50 |
| (b) Correct marking-coloured bell and shield, no arms | | 56mm | | 56.50 |
| (c) White glazed | | 153mm | 27.50 | 32.50 |
| (d) White glazed, brown trim, blue and red shields on white glazed ground | | 153mm | | 800.00 |
| (e) Matt black with multi-coloured bells, no arms | | 153mm | | 875.00 |
| Matching Arms: *LINCOLN* | | | | |
| | | | | |
| **LINCOLN VASE** | | 67mm | 8.00 | 23.00 |
| Matching Arms: *LINCOLN* | | 88mm | 15.00 | 28.00 |
| | | | | |
| **LITTLEHAMPTON ROMAN EWER** | | 73mm | 10.50 | 23.00 |
| Matching Arms: *LITTLEHAMPTON* | | | | |
| | | | | |
| **LLANDUDNO (LITTLE ORME) ROMAN VASE** | | 82mm | 17.00 | 28.00 |
| Matching Arms: *LLANDUDNO* | | | | |
| | | | | |
| **LLANDUDNO (GOGARTH) ANCIENT VASE** | | 84mm | 17.00 | 28.00 |
| Matching Arms: *LLANDUDNO* | | | | |
| | | | | |
| **LLANGOLLEN CORACLE** | | Length 77mm | 21.50 | 37.50 |
| Matching Arms: *LLANGOLLEN* | | | | |
| See also WELSH CORACLE | | | | |
| | | | | |
| **LOBSTER TRAP** | | 51mm | 18.50 | 33.50 |
| Matching Arms: *ANY OF THE CHANNEL ISLANDS* | | 84mm[1] | 34.50 | 47.50 |
| *(ALDERNEY, GUERNSEY, JERSEY, SARK) OR* | | | | |
| *BOGNOR.* | | | | |
| **LONDON CHRIST'S HOSPITAL ENGLISH WINE FLAGON** | | 90mm | 11.50 | 21.50 |
| Matching Arms: *CHRIST'S HOSPITAL OR CITY OF LONDON* | | | | |
| | | | | |
| **LONDON STONE** | (a) White† | 109mm | 150.00 | |
| | (b) Brown† | 109mm | 200.00 | |
| | | | | |
| **LONGSHIPS LIGHTHOUSE, LAND'S END** | | 122mm | 40.00 | 75.00 |
| Matching Arms: *LAND'S END* | | | | |
| | | | | |
| **LOOE EWER** | | 65mm | 7.50 | 21.50 |
| Matching Arms: *LOOE OR EAST LOOE OR WEST LOOE EAST* | | | | |
| | | | | |
| **LOUTH ANCIENT EWER** | | 43mm | 7.50 | 22.50 |
| Matching Arms: *LOUTH* | | 113mm | 24.50 | 40.00 |
| | | | | |
| **LUDLOW SACK BOTTLE** | a) With 1 coat of arms | 75mm[1] | 15.50 | 27.50 |
| Matching Arms: *LUDLOW* | b) With 3 coats of arms | 75mm[1] | 20.00 | 35.00 |

| Model | | With any Arms £ p | With Matching Arms £ p |
|---|---|---|---|
| **LUTON BOTTLE OR COSTREL** <br> Matching Arms: *LUTON* | Length 65mm | 14.50 | 30.00 |
| **LYME REGIS AMMONITE** <br> Matching Arms: *LYME REGIS* | 73mm | 40.00 | 72.50 |
| **MADEIRA BULLOCK CAR** <br> Matching Arms: *FUNCHAL, MADEIRA* | 58mm | | 1800.00 |
| **MAIDSTONE ROMAN EWER** <br> Matching Arms: *MAIDSTONE* | 82mm <br> 130mm | 9.00 <br> 27.50 | 19.50 <br> 33.50 |
| **MALDON (ESSEX) GERMAN INCENDIARY BOMB** <br> This model has a delicate handle which is frequently found broken, in which condition it is of little value. <br> Matching Arms: *MALDON* | 75mm | 26.00 | 40.00 |

**Either MALTA or VALLETTA would be considered matching on any Maltese Model**

| Model | | With any Arms £ p | With Matching Arms £ p |
|---|---|---|---|
| **MALTESE CARAFE** <br> Matching Arms: *MALTA* | 105mm | 21.50 | 40.00 |
| **MALTESE DOUBLE-MOUTHED VASE** <br> Matching Arms: *MALTA* | 60mm | 33.50 | 47.00 |
| **MALTESE FIRE GRATE** <br> Matching Arms: *MALTA* | 53mm | 17.00 | 24.50 |
| **MALTESE FUNEREAL URN** <br> Matching Arms: *MALTA* | 61mm | 9.00 | 25.00 |
| **MALTESE TWIN VASE** <br> Matching Arms: *MALTA* | 50mm | 40.00 | 56.50 |
| **MALTESE TWO-WICK LAMP** <br> Matching Arms: *MALTA* | Length 81mm | 17.00 | 27.50 |
| **MALTESE VASE à CANARD** <br> Matching Arms: *MALTA* | 45mm | 20.50 | 37.50 |
| **MANX LOBSTER POT** <br> Matching Arms: *ISLE OF MAN* OR *ANY MANX ARMS* | Dia. 67mm | | 47.00 |
| **MANX PEEL POT** <br> Matching Arms: *ISLE OF MAN* OR *ANY MANX ARMS* | 49mm | 12.50 | 28.50 |

| Model | | | With any Arms £ p | With Matching Arms £ p |
|---|---|---|---|---|
| **(ANCIENT) MANX SPIRIT MEASURE** | | 68mm | 14.00 | 30.00 |
| Matching Arms: *ISLE OF MAN* OR *ANY MANX ARMS* | | | | |
| **(THE) MAPLE LEAF OF CANADA** | | 118mm | 70.00 | 145.00 |
| Matching Arms: *ANY CANADIAN ARMS* OR *B.E.E. WEMBLEY* | | | | |
| **MARY QUEEN OF SCOTS** | | | | |
| Face in high relief on (a) two-piece night-light | | 78mm | 130.00 | 160.00 |
| (b) two or three-handled mug | | 118mm | 87.50 | 145.00 |
| Correct Arms: *MARY QUEEN OF SCOTS* | | | | |
| **MELROSE CUP** | | 128mm | 47.50 | 65.00 |
| Matching Arms: *MELROSE ABBEY* OR *MELROSE* | | | | |
| **MINSTER ANCIENT EWER** | | 88mm | 23.00 | 40.00 |
| Matching Arms: *MINSTER* | | | | |
| **MINSTER ANCIENT URN** | | 65mm | 11.50 | 35.00 |
| Matching Arms: *MINSTER* | | | | |
| **MONS MEG, EDINBURGH CASTLE** | Length 122mm | | 34.50 | 47.00 |
| Matching Arms: *EDINBURGH* | | | | |
| **MUNICH BEER SEIDEL** | | 52mm | 75.00 | 125.00 |
| Matching Arms: *MUNICH (MÜNCHEN)* | | | | |
| **MUSSELBURGH KIRKPARK ANCIENT URN** | | 51mm | 7.50 | 26.00 |
| Matching Arms: *MUSSELBURGH* | | | | |
| **NATIONAL HIGHLAND CUACH or WHISKEY CUP** | | | | |
| Any Highland Arms are considered matching. | | Width 94mm | 14.00 | 16.00 |
| **NEWBURY LEATHER BOTTLE** | | | | |
| (a) | | 58mm | 7.50 | 16.00 |
| (b) | | 114mm[1] | 22.00 | 32.50 |
| (c) With Stopper | | 125mm[1] | 41.50 | 56.50 |
| First Period examples of the larger size have a thicker rim to take a porcelain and cork stopper, whilst Second Period models are thinner and no stopper was included, nor indeed will fit. Matching Arms: *BURGUS NEWBERIE* | | | | |
| **NEWCASTLE (STAFFORDSHIRE) CUP** | | 70mm[1] | 30.00 | 40.00 |
| Matching Arms: *NEWCASTLE-UNDER-LYME* | | | | |
| **NEWCASTLE CASTLE** | (a) White glazed | 88mm | 150.00 | 350.00 |
| Matching Arms: *NEWCASTLE* | (b) Brown† | 88mm | 525.00 | |

| Model | | | With any Arms £ p | With Matching Arms £ p |
|---|---|---|---|---|
| **NEWCASTLE ROMAN JUG** | | 63mm | 6.50 | 16.00 |
| Matching Arms: *NEWCASTLE* | | | | |
| **NORTH FORELAND LIGHTHOUSE** | | 108mm | 72.50 | 85.00 |
| Matching Arms: *BROADSTAIRS OR RAMSGATE OR MARGATE* | | | | |
| **NORWEGIAN BUCKET** | | 58mm | 14.50 | 56.50 |
| Matching Arms: *NORWAY (NORGE)* | | | | |
| **NORWEGIAN DRAGON-SHAPED BEER BOWL** | | | | |
| Matching Arms: *NORWAY (NORGE)* | | Length 155mm | 29.50 | 56.50 |
| With Norwegian inscription | | Length 155mm | | 75.00 |
| **NORWEGIAN HORSE-SHAPED BEER BOWL** | | | | |
| Matching Arms: *NORWAY (NORGE)* | | Length 115mm | 25.00 | 56.50 |
| With Norwegian inscription | | Length 115mm | | 75.00 |
| **NORWEGIAN WOODEN SHOE** | | | | |
| Matching Arms: *NORWAY (NORGE)* | | Length 103mm | 25.00 | 47.50 |
| With Norwegian inscription | | Length 103mm | | 70.00 |

**The Arms of any Norwegian Town would also be considered matching. BERGEN is the most common, followed by Trondheim with the Norwegian spelling TRONDHJEM**

| Model | | | With any Arms £ p | With Matching Arms £ p |
|---|---|---|---|---|
| **NORWICH URN** | | 51mm | 6.50 | 15.50 |
| Matching Arms: *NORWICH* | | 62mm | 9.50 | 19.50 |
| | | 90mm[1] | 14.50 | 31.50 |
| **NOTTINGHAM EWER** | a) With one coat of arms 63mm | | 7.00 | 21.00 |
| Matching Arms: | b) With two coats of arms 63mm | | 7.50 | 25.00 |
| *NOTTINGHAM* | | | | |
| **NOTTINGHAM URN** | | 40mm | 6.50 | 20.50 |
| Matching Arms: *NOTTINGHAM* | | | | |
| **OLD GATEWAY ON MONNOW BRIDGE** | | | | |
| Matching Arms: *MONMOUTH* | (a) White glazed | 95mm | 85.00 | 255.00 |
| | (b) Brown† | 95mm | 215.00 | |
| **ORKNEY CRAISIE** | | 80mm | 19.50 | 40.00 |
| Matching Arms: *COUNTY OF ORKNEY OR KIRKWALL* | | | | |
| **OSTEND FLEMISH BOTTLE** | | 65mm | 9.00 | 23.00 |
| Matching Arms: *OSTENDE* | | | | |
| **OSTEND FLEMISH TOBACCO JAR** | | 54mm | 7.50 | 26.00 |
| Matching Arms: *OSTENDE* | | | | |

| Model | | | With any Arms £ p | With Matching Arms £ p |
|---|---|---|---|---|
| **OSTEND VASE** | | 57mm | 7.50 | 21.50 |
| Matching Arms: *OSTENDE* | | | | |
| **OXFORD EWER** | | 76mm | 8.50 | 15.50 |
| Matching Arms: *CITY OF OXFORD* with *EXETER* | | 126mm[1] | 21.00 | 30.00 |
| College Oxford perhaps being considered the next appropriate. | | | | |
| **OXFORD JUG** | | 173mm[1] | 23.00 | 40.00 |
| Matching Arms: *CITY OF OXFORD* with *TRINITY* College | | | | |
| Oxford perhaps being considered the next appropriate. | | | | |
| **PAINSWICK POT** | | 50mm | 6.50 | 22.50 |
| Matching Arms: *PAINSWICK* | | | | |
| **PANAMA VASE** | | 130mm | 33.00 | |
| Matching Arms: *PANAMA*, but not yet seen on this model. | | | | |
| **PENMAENMAWR URN** | | 45mm | 6.50 | 19.50 |
| Matching Arms: *PENMAENMAWR* | | | | |
| **PERTH CORONATION CHAIR** | (a) White glazed | 85mm | 82.50 | 110.00 |
| Matching Arms: *PERTH* | (b) Stone in brown | 85mm | 117.50 | 170.00 |
| | (c) Brown† | 85mm | 285.00 | |
| **PETERBOROUGH TRIPOD** | (a) 1 coat of arms | 47mm | 11.00 | 18.50 |
| Matching Arms: *PETERBOROUGH* | (b) 2 coats of arms | 47mm | 17.00 | 25.00 |
| **PLYMOUTH (SPANISH) JUG** | | 55mm | 6.50 | 21.00 |
| Matching arms: *PLYMOUTH, DEVONPORT* OR *STONEHOUSE* | | | | |
| **POMPEIAN EWER** | | 91mm | 10.00 | |
| Both sizes are found unnamed | | 208mm | 34.50 | |
| Italian Arms have yet to be recorded on this model, but | | | | |
| they would certainly be considered matching were they to exist. | | | | |
| **PORTLAND LIGHTHOUSE** | (a) Plain | 120mm | 26.00 | |
| Matching Arms: *THE ISLAND &* | (b) Brown band | 120mm | 75.00 | 82.50 |
| *ROYAL MANOR OF PORTLAND* | (c) Orange band | 120mm | 100.00 | 140.00 |
| *URBAN DISTRICT COUNCIL* | | | | |
| **PORTLAND VASE** | | | | |
| With Josiah Wedgwood Memorial inscription | | (a) 51mm | 7.00 | 30.00 |
| Matching Arms: *(a) DUKE OF PORTLAND* | | (b) 51mm | 26.00 | 65.00 |
| *(b) JOSIAH WEDGWOOD* | | | | |
| **PRESTON OLD BUSHEL MEASURE** | | Dia. 58mm | 100.00 | 200.00 |
| Matching Arms: *PRESTON* | | | | |

| Model | | | With any Arms £   p | With Matching Arms £   p |
|---|---|---|---|---|
| **QUEEN ELIZABETH'S RIDING SHOE** | Length 105mm | | 95.00 | 117.50 |
| Matching Arms: *THAXTED* | | | | |
| **QUEEN PHILIPPA'S RECORD CHEST** | | | | |
| | Length (a) 80mm | | 32.00 | 47.00 |
| Matching Arms: *KNARESBOROUGH (ABBEY)* | (b) 94mm | | 34.00 | 50.00 |
| **QUEEN VICTORIA'S FIRST SHOE** | | | | |
| | (a) Without Arms | 102mm | 35.00† | |
| | (b) Pre-1901 | 102mm | 26.00 | 35.00 |
| | (c) Post-1901 | 102mm | 26.00 | 35.00 |
| A descriptive leaflet was issued with this model and is valued at £15.00. | | | | |
| Matching Arms: *H.M. QUEEN VICTORIA* OR *SIDMOUTH* | | | | |
| **RAMSEY CRONK AUST CINERARY URN** | 59mm | | 12.50 | 22.50 |
| Matching Arms: *RAMSEY, ISLE OF MAN* | | | | |
| **RAMSGATE ROMANO-BRITISH EWER** | 47mm | | 23.00 | 46.00 |
| Matching Arms: *RAMSGATE* | | | | |
| **RAMSGATE ROMANO-BRITISH JUG** | 70mm | | 14.50 | 40.00 |
| Matching Arms: *RAMSGATE* | | | | |
| **RAMSGATE URN** | 75mm | | 15.00 | 36.00 |
| Matching Arms: *RAMSGATE* | | | | |
| **RAYLEIGH ANCIENT COOKING POT** | 33mm | | 7.00 | 30.00 |
| Matching Arms: *RAYLEIGH* | | | | |
| **READING JUG** | 82mm | | 6.50 | 14.00 |
| Matching Arms: *READING* | 140mm | | 19.50 | 27.50 |
| **READING (SILCHESTER) URN** | 50mm | | 6.50 | 14.00 |
| Matching Arms: *READING* | | | | |
| **READING (SILCHESTER) VASE** | 50mm | | 6.50 | 15.50 |
| Matching Arms: *READING* | | | | |
| **ROCHESTER BELLARMINE JUG** | 65mm | | 7.00 | 19.50 |
| Matching Arms: *ROCHESTER* | | | | |
| **ROMAN MORTARIUM** | Dia. 95mm | (a) Named | 75.00 | |
| This model has no matching arms. | | (b) Unnamed | 30.00 | |
| **ROMAN VASE** | (a) White glazed | 160mm | 47.50 | |
| It has no matching arms | (b) Lustre† | 160mm | 75.00 | |

| Model | | | With any Arms £ p | With Matching Arms £ p |
|---|---|---|---|---|
| **ROMSEY BUSHEL** | | Dia. 68mm | 16.50 | 34.50 |
| Matching Arms: *ROMSEY* | | | | |
| **ROTHESAY STONE** | Brown† | Length 95mm Width 25mm | 1250.00 | |
| **RUFUS STONE** | | 94mm | 12.00 | 19.50 |
| Occasionally appears with no arms | | | 10.00 | |
| Matching Arms: *KING WILLIAM RUFUS* | | | | |
| **RUSSIAN SHRAPNEL SHELL** | | 110mm | 25.00 | 56.50 |
| Matching Arms: *RUSSIA* OR *ANY ARTILLERY REGIMENT* | | | | |
| **RYE CANNON BALL, Multi-coloured** | | | | |
| Matching Arms: *RYE* | (a) On plinth | 106mm | 75.00 | 125.00 |
| | (b) Without plinth | 68mm | 40.00 | 65.00 |
| **SAFFRON WALDEN COVERED URN and lid** | | 70mm | 21.00 | 40.00 |
| This model has a lid that looks very like an Egyptian | | 121mm | 28.50 | 43.00 |
| Mummy's Head without which it is incomplete, value £8.00 | | | | |
| Matching Arms: *SAFFRON WALDEN* | | | | |
| With any Egyptian Arms add £10.00 | | | | |
| **ST. ALBANS ANCIENT COOKING POT** | | 58mm | 16.00 | 28.00 |
| Matching Arms: *ST. ALBANS* | | | | |
| **ST. MARY'S LIGHTHOUSE, WHITLEY BAY** | | 135mm | 550.00 | 750.00 |
| Matching Arms: *DUKE OF NORTHUMBERLAND: MANOR OF WHITLEY BAY* | | | | |
| **ST. NEOTS ANCIENT URN** | | 63mm | 8.00 | 26.00 |
| Matching Arms: *ST. NEOTS* | | | | |
| **ST. SIMON OF SUDBURY'S SKULL** | (a) White† | 72mm | 175.00 | |
| | (b) Brown† | 72mm | 285.00 | |
| **SALISBURY KETTLE** | | 88mm | 15.50 | 24.50 |
| Matching Arms: *SALISBURY* | | 133mm | 17.50 | 32.50 |
| **SALISBURY LEATHER JACK** | | 44mm | 7.00 | 19.50 |
| The large size is always, and the small size is | | 80mm | | 300.00 |
| sometimes found with C R 1646 on the side under a | | 140mm[1] | 23.00 | 40.00 |
| crown. In addition, it appears both crested and | | | | |
| uncrested. Same price. | | | | |
| Matching Arms: *SALISBURY* | | | | |

| Model | | | With any Arms £   p | With Matching Arms £   p |
|---|---|---|---|---|
| **SALISBURY LEATHER GILL** | | 75mm | 14.50 | 26.00 |
| This model is always found with RSM 1658 in red and blue letters on the side. It can be found both crested and uncrested. Same price. Matching Arms: *SALISBURY* | | | | |
| **SARK FISH BASKET** | | 45mm | | 65.00 |
| Matching Arms: *SARK (SERCQ)* | | 58mm | | 75.00 |
| **SARK MILK CAN and lid** | | 70mm | 20.00 | 56.50 |
| This would be incomplete without its lid, value £10.00. | | 108mm | | 56.50 |
| Matching Arms: *SARK (SERCQ)* | | 140mm | | 65.00 |
| **SCARBOROUGH JUG** | | 51mm | 6.50 | 13.00 |
| Matching Arms: *SCARBOROUGH* | | 70mm | 14.00 | 22.50 |
| **SCARBOROUGH KETTLE** | | 65mm | 12.50 | 21.00 |
| Matching Arms: *SCARBOROUGH* | | 88mm | 18.50 | 31.50 |
| **SEAFORD URN** | a) With one coat of arms | 48mm | 10.50 | 17.50 |
| Matching Arms: *SEAFORD* | b) With two coats of arms | 48mm | 15.00 | 25.00 |
| **SHAKESPEARE'S JUG** | | 58mm | 17.50 | 22.50 |
| Matching Arms: *WILLIAM SHAKESPEARE* OR | | 76mm | 20.00 | 30.00 |
| *STRATFORD-ON-AVON* | | 88mm | 25.00 | 40.00 |
| **SHREWSBURY (URICONIUM) EWER** | | | | |
| | a) With one or two coats of arms | 100mm [1] | 27.50 | 34.50 |
| | b) With three coats of arms | 100mm [1] | 35.00 | 45.00 |
| Matching Arms: *SHREWSBURY* | | | | |
| **SHREWSBURY ROMANO-SALOPIAN EWER** | | 68mm | 7.00 | 21.50 |
| Matching Arms: *SHREWSBURY* | | | | |
| **SIR JOHN BARROW'S MONUMENT ULVERSTON** | | 120mm | 115.00 | 160.00 |
| Matching Arms: *ULVERSTON* | | | | |
| **SKEGNESS CLOCK TOWER** | | 132mm | 105.00 | 145.00 |
| Matching Arms: *SKEGNESS* | | | | |
| **SOUTHAMPTON ANCIENT PIPKIN** | | 56mm | 7.00 | 13.00 |
| Matching Arms: *SOUTHAMPTON* | | 76mm | 17.50 | 28.00 |
| | | 101mm[1] | 23.00 | 35.00 |

| Model | | | With any Arms £ p | With Matching Arms £ p |
|---|---|---|---|---|
| **SOUTHAMPTON BARGATE** | | | | |
| Matching Arms: | (a) Small, white glazed | 55mm | 47.50 | 105.00 |
| *SOUTHAMPTON* | (b) Small, grey† | 55mm | 87.50 | |
| | (c) Large, white glazed | 87mm | 65.00 | 145.00 |
| | (d) Large, grey† | 87mm | 165.00 | |
| | (e) Large, brown† | 87mm | 185.00 | |
| | (f) Large, white, unglazed† | 87mm | 145.00 | |

**SOUTHDOWN SHEEP BELL**      54mm    65.00    105.00
This model is identical to the Small Swiss Cow Bell and is
incomplete without the loose porcelain clapper suspended
inside it, worth £10.00 alone.
It has no correct arms - any Sussex Downland arms are to be
considered as matching

| Model | Size | With any Arms | With Matching Arms |
|---|---|---|---|
| **SOUTHPORT VASE** <br> Matching Arms: *SOUTHPORT* | 50mm | 7.00 | 17.00 |
| **SOUTHWOLD ANCIENT GUN** <br> Matching Arms: *SOUTHWOLD* | Length 94mm | 125.00 | 190.00 |
| **SOUTHWOLD JAR** <br> Matching Arms: *SOUTHWOLD* | 88mm <br> 140mm[1] | 7.00 <br> 25.00 | 20.50 <br> 40.00 |
| **(STAFFORDSHIRE) ONE-HANDLED TYG** <br> Matching Arms: *STAFFORDSHIRE* | 65mm | 6.50 | 24.50 |
| **(STAFFORDSHIRE) TWO-HANDLED TYG** <br> Matching Arms: *STAFFORDSHIRE* | 65mm | 6.50 | 24.50 |
| **STEYNING SHEPHERD'S CROWN SEA URCHIN** <br> Matching Arms: *STEYNING* | 50mm | 30.00 | 52.00 |
| **STIRLING PINT MEASURE** <br> Matching Arms: *STIRLING* | 61mm | 14.00 | 30.00 |
| **STOCKPORT PLAGUE STONE** <br> Matching Arms: *STOCKPORT* | Length 75mm | 30.00 | 47.50 |
| **STOCKTON ANCIENT SALT POT** <br> Matching Arms: *STOCKTON-ON-TEES* | 73mm | 10.00 | 30.00 |
| **STORNOWAY HIGHLAND MILK CROGAN** <br> Matching Arms: *STORNOWAY* | 56mm | 10.50 | 35.00 |
| **STRATFORD-ON-AVON SANCTUARY KNOCKER** <br> **in high relief on two-handled mug**   Height of detail <br> Matching Arms: *STRATFORD-ON-AVON* | 62mm | 145.00 | 225.00 |

| Model | | | With any Arms £ p | With Matching Arms £ p |
|---|---|---|---|---|
| **STRATFORD-ON-AVON TOBY BASIN** | | | | |
| **Multi-coloured** | | 53mm | 85.00† | |
| | | | | |
| **STRATFORD-ON-AVON TOBY JUG** | | | | |
| **Multi-coloured** | | 78mm | 105.00† | |

The above two models are a pair.

| Model | | | With any Arms £ p | With Matching Arms £ p |
|---|---|---|---|---|
| **SUNDERLAND BOTTLE** | | 58mm | 6.50 | 19.50 |
| Matching Arms: *SUNDERLAND* | | | | |
| **SWINDON VASE** | | 55mm | 6.50 | 24.50 |
| Matching Arms: *SWINDON* | | 110mm[1] | 14.00 | 28.00 |
| **SWISS COW BELL** | | 51mm | 13.00 | 34.50 |
| Matching Arms: *SWITZERLAND* or any Arms from that | | 73mm | 19.50 | 40.00 |
| country. Incomplete without clapper priced individually at £10.00 | | | | |
| **SWISS MILK BUCKET** | | 56mm | 14.00 | 37.50 |
| Matching Arms: *SWITZERLAND* or any Arms from that | | 82mm | 21.00 | 41.50 |
| country | | | | |
| **SWISS MILK POT and lid** | | 82mm | 17.00 | 47.50 |
| This model is incomplete without its lid which is | | | | |
| valued at £7.00. | | | | |
| Matching Arms: *SWITZERLAND* or any Arms from that | | | | |
| country | | | | |
| **SWISS VINEGAR BOTTLE** | | Length 75mm | 13.00 | 45.00 |
| Matching Arms: *SWITZERLAND* or any Arms from that | | | | |
| country | | | | |
| **TEIGNMOUTH LIGHTHOUSE** | | 118mm | 72.50 | 82.50 |
| Matching Arms: *TEIGNMOUTH* | | | | |
| **TENBY GATEWAY** | (a) White glazed | 65mm | 175.00 | 215.00 |
| Matching Arms: *TENBY* | (b) Brown | 65mm | 175.00 | 330.00 |
| | (c) Brown | 65mm | 330.00† | |
| **TEWKESBURY SAXON URN** | | 45mm | 6.50 | 23.00 |
| Matching Arms: *TEWKESBURY* | | | | |
| **TINTERN ANCIENT WATER BOTTLE** | | 76mm | 11.50 | 30.00 |
| Matching Arms: *TINTERN ABBEY* OR *CHEPSTOW* | | | | |
| **TONBRIDGE EASTCHEAP ROMAN EWER** | | 63mm | 9.00 | 23.00 |
| Matching Arms: *TONBRIDGE* | | | | |

| Model | | | With any Arms £ p | With Matching Arms £ p |
|---|---|---|---|---|
| **TRESCO OLD BRAZIER** Matching Arms: *F ALGERNON DORRIEN-SMITH, LORD PROPRIETOR OF THE ISLES OF SCILLY* | 69mm | | 16.00 | 42.00 |
| **TRESVANNACK ANCIENT URN** Matching Arms: *PENZANCE (PENSANS A.D.)* | 55mm | | 10.50 | 22.50 |
| **TRURO GLEN DORGAL CINERARY URN** Matching Arms: *TRURO* | 54mm | | 9.00 | 26.00 |
| **TUSCAN VASE** It has no matching arms | (a) White glazed (b) Lustre (orange or yellow) | 150mm 150mm | 125.00 160.00 | |
| **TWICKENHAM ANTIQUE POPE'S PIPE** Matching Arms: *TWICKENHAM* | | Length 118mm | 30.00 | 47.00 |
| **WALMER ROMAN VASE** Matching Arms: *WALMER OR DEAL* | 65mm | | 6.50 | 19.50 |
| **WAREHAM BOTTLE** Matching Arms: *WAREHAM* | 67mm | | 7.00 | 19.50 |
| **WATERLOOVILLE SOLDIER'S WATER BOTTLE** Matching Arms: *WATERLOOVILLE* | 83mm | | 22.50 | 30.00 |

**Any Welsh arms may be considered matching on Welsh models**

| Model | | | With any Arms £ p | With Matching Arms £ p |
|---|---|---|---|---|
| **WELSH CORACLE** Matching Arms: *LLANGOLLEN OR ANY WELSH ARMS* | | Length 77mm | 25.00 | 33.50 |
| **WELSH CROCHON** (**N.B.** The Welsh word for cauldron is spelt Crochon) Matching Arms: *CONWAY* | | 50mm 61mm 76mm[1] 107mm[1] 115mm[1] | 12.50 14.00 17.00 28.50 31.50 | 22.50 25.00 30.00 65.00 75.00 |
| **WELSH FISH BASKET** Matching Arms: *ARMS OF WALES OR ANY WELSH ARMS* | 58mm | | | 85.00 |
| **WELSH HAT** Matching Arms: *ARMS OF WALES OR ANY WELSH ARMS* | (a) Plain brim (b) Llanfair P.G. on brim | Dia. 74mm | 17.50 30.00 | 30.00 45.00 |
| **WELSH JACK and lid** This model is not complete without its lid, value £10.00. Matching Arms: *ARMS OF WALES OR ANY WELSH ARMS* | 120mm | | 21.00 | 45.00 |

| Model | | With any Arms £   p | With Matching Arms £   p |
|---|---|---|---|
| **WELSH LEEK** | 90mm | 19.50 | 30.00 |

This model has six leaf tips each coloured green.
Matching Arms: *ARMS OF WALES OR ANY WELSH ARMS*

| **WELSH MILK CAN and lid** | 70mm | 15.00 | 30.00 |
|---|---|---|---|
| The model is incomplete without its lid | 108mm | 30.00 | 47.50 |
| which is worth £10.00 | 130mm | 30.00 | 56.50 |
| | 140mm | 30.00 | 56.50 |

Matching Arms: *ARMS OF WALES OR ANY WELSH ARMS*

| **WELSH PICYN** | 62mm | 15.50 | 32.00 |
|---|---|---|---|

Matching Arms: *ARMS OF WALES OR ANY WELSH ARMS*

| **WENSLEYDALE LEYBURN LEATHER JACK** | 67mm | 12.50 | 30.00 |
|---|---|---|---|

Matching Arms: *LEYBURN*

**WESTMINSTER ABBEY CORONATION CHAIR**
See also Perth Coronation Chair
Two varieties, one with hole in rear;
one without and gilded

| (a) White | 85mm | 40.00 | 56.50 |
|---|---|---|---|
| (b) Stone in brown | 85mm | 82.50 | 117.50 |
| (c) Brown | 85mm | 250.00† | 285.00 |

A blue version is thought to exist, but has not yet been seen.
Matching Arms: *WESTMINSTER ABBEY*

| **WEYMOUTH ROMAN VASE** | 56mm | 7.50 | 19.50 |
|---|---|---|---|
| Matching Arms: *WEYMOUTH* | 94mm[1] | 20.50 | 32.50 |

| **WHITBY AMMONITE** | 73mm | 34.50 | 56.50 |
|---|---|---|---|

Identical to the rarer Lyme Regis Ammonite
Matching Arms: *WHITBY*

| **WHITBY PILLION STONE** | Length 72mm | 30.00 | 47.50 |
|---|---|---|---|

Matching Arms: *WHITBY*

| **WHITSTABLE ROMAN PATERA** | Dia. 88mm | 21.50 | 40.00 |
|---|---|---|---|

Matching Arms: *THE SEAL OF THE CORPORATION
OF THE DREDGERS OF WHITSTABLE, 1793*

| Model | | | With any Arms £ p | With Matching Arms £ p |
|---|---|---|---|---|
| **WINCHESTER BUSHEL** | 100mm across Height 38mm | | 155.00† | 190.00 |
| Decorated with red and blue lettering | Height 51mm | | 125.00† | 265.00 |
| in relief, and various symbols. | 145mm across Height 65mm[1] | | 400.00† | 500.00 |
| The largest size is normally unmarked. | | | | |
| Matching Arms: *WINCHESTER* | | | | |
| There is also a rare First Period example, unglazed, | | | | |
| with pale blue legs, brushed gilding, red and blue | | | | |
| lettering in relief. | | | | |
| | 170mm across Height 70mm[1] | | | 500.00 |
| **WINCHESTER FLAGON** | | 100mm[1] | 26.00 | 45.00 |
| Matching Arms: *WINCHESTER* | | 130mm[1] | 26.00 | 65.00 |
| | | 152mm[1] | 36.00 | 85.00 |
| **WINCHESTER JACK** | | 32mm | 17.50 | 28.50 |
| Matching Arms: *WINCHESTER* | | 44mm | 6.50 | 17.50 |
| | | 83mm | 14.00 | 25.00 |
| | | 121mm[1] | 21.50 | 40.00 |
| **WINCHESTER POT** | | 74mm | 19.50 | 26.00 |
| Matching Arms: *WINCHESTER* | | | | |
| **WINCHESTER QUART** | | 92mm†[1] | 810.00 | |
| This model is not known bearing a coat of arms, but carries | | | | |
| an embossed crown and 1601 E.R on its side. It is a | | | | |
| most impressive piece - rare and desirable. | | | | |
| **WINCHESTER CASTLE WARDER'S HORN** | | Length | | |
| | (a) on plinth† | 152mm [1] | 565.00 | |
| | (b) without plinth† | 152mm [1] | 400.00 | |
| **WINDLESHAW CHANTRY** | | 128mm | 85.00 | 160.00 |
| Matching Arms: *EN DIEU EST MON ESPERANCE* | | | | |
| **WINDSOR KETTLE and lid** | | 170mm | 140.00 | 170.00 |
| This model should have a circular lid with a flat top | | | | |
| surmounted by a round knob. Value £50.00 | | | | |
| Matching Arms: *WINDSOR* | | | | |
| **WINDSOR ROUND TOWER** | (a) Large white† | 145mm | 550.00 | |
| | (b) Large brown† | 145mm | 650.00 | |
| | (c) Large grey† | 145mm | 525.00 | |
| **WINDSOR URN** | | 45mm | 7.50 | 12.50 |
| Matching Arms: *WINDSOR* OR *ETON (FLOREAT ETONA)* | | 82mm | 21.50 | 30.00 |

| Model | | | With any Arms £ p | With Matching Arms £ p |
|---|---|---|---|---|
| **WINSFORD SALT LUMP** This is identical to the Cheshire Salt Block, and appears with the Arms of Winsford either glazed or unglazed (a). A rare variety (b) has been seen with holes for pouring in the top and SALT in Gothic script on the front. Matching Arms: *WINSFORD* | (a) 80mm (b) 80mm | | | 82.50 100.00 |
| **WISBECH JUG** Matching Arms: *WISBECH* | 82mm[1] | | 27.50 | 56.50 |
| **WITCH'S CAULDRON** This model is identical to the Peterborough Tripod Matching with Scottish, Shakespeare's arms or *STRATFORD-ON-AVON* | 47mm | | 23.00 | 35.00 |
| **WORCESTER JUG** Matching Arms: *WORCESTER* | 64mm 101mm[1] | | 10.50 17.00 | 17.50 26.00 |
| **WYMONDHAM ANCIENT JAR** Matching Arms: *WYMONDHAM* | 61mm | | 15.00 | 30.00 |
| **YARMOUTH EWER** Matching Arms: *GREAT YARMOUTH* | 62mm | | 7.00 | 15.50 |
| **YARMOUTH JUG** Matching Arms: *GREAT YARMOUTH* | 132mm | | 56.50 | 80.00 |
| **YORICK'S SKULL** The 102mm version is in two pieces and is designed for use as a night-light, the base modelled as three books. | (a) Pale yellow† (b) White unglazed† (c) Pale yellow† (d) White unglazed† (e) Pale yellow† (f) White glazed† | 38mm 75mm 75mm 102mm 102mm 102mm | 75.00 95.50 170.00 125.00 175.00 130.00 | |
| **YORK ROMAN EWER** Matching Arms: *YORK* | 63mm 127mm[1] | | 7.00 · 22.50 | 20.50 30.00 |
| **YORK ROMAN URN** Matching Arms: *YORK* | 51mm 101mm[1] | | 6.50 14.50 | 15.00 30.00 |
| **YORK ROMAN VESSEL** Matching Ams: *YORK* | 73mm[1] | | 18.50 | 30.00 |

# MODELS

| | |
|---|---|
| *Top row* | Folkestone Saltwood Roman Ewer, Pompeian Ewer, Irish Mather, Japan Ewer, Lincoln Jack, Boston Ancient Ewer, Burton Beer Barrel. |
| *Second row* | Salisbury Leather Gill, Ancient Manx Spirit Measure, Minster Ancient Ewer, Oxford Ewer, Newbury Leather Bottle, Canterbury Leather Bottle, Winchester Jacks. |
| *Third row* | Burton Beer Barrel, Gibraltar Alcaraza, Rochester Bellarmine Jug, Salisbury Leather Jack, National Highland Cuach, Tintern Ancient Water Bottle, Ipswich Ancient Ewer. |
| *Fourth row* | Carnarvon Ewer, Goodwin Sands Carafe, Doncaster Ewer, Shrewsbury Romano-Salopian Ewer, Felixstowe Roman Ewer, Devon Oak Pitcher, Yarmouth Ewer. |

# MODELS

| | |
|---|---|
| *Top row* | Ludlow Sack Bottle, Welsh Hat, Guildford Roman Vase, Bournemouth Bronze Urn. |
| *Second row* | Jersey Fish Basket, Luton Costrel, Kininmonth Moss Ancient Pot, Newcastle Roman Jug, Winchester Jack, Caerleon Glass Lachrymatory. |
| *Third row* | Norwegian Dragon-shaped Beer Bowl, Norwegian Bucket, Norwegian Horse-shaped Beer Bowl. |

# MODELS

| | |
|---|---|
| *Top row* | Swiss Milk Bucket, Egyptian Alabaster Bowl No. 9, Maltese Carafe, Ostend Flemish Tobacco Jar, Egyptian Water Jar, Russian Shrapnel Shell. |
| *Second row* | Las Palmas Ancient Covered Jarra, Egyptian Mocha Cup, Dinant Wooden Shoe, Las Palmas Ancient Earthen Jar, Boulogne Milk Can, Las Palmas Ancient Jarra, Maltese Fire Gate |
| *Third row* | Maltese Two-wick Lamp, Swiss Cow Bell, Boulogne Sedan Chair, Swiss Cow Bell, Egyptian Mocha Cup, Dutch Sabot. |
| *Fourth Row* | Norwegian Bucket, Ostend Vase, Swiss Milk Pot, Ostend Flemish Bottle, Las Palmas Ancient Jarra, Maltese Two-wick Lamp. |

# MODELS

| | |
|---|---|
| *Top row* | Kendal Jug, Itford Lewes Urn, Leek Urn, Eton Vase |
| *Second row* | Hornsea Atwick Roman Vase, Irish Wooden Noggin, Lincoln Vase, Brixworth Ancient Cup. |
| *Third row* | Glastonbury Roman Ewer, Manx Peel Pot, Fountains Abbey Abbot's Cup, Hunstanton Ewer. |

# MODELS

| | |
|---|---|
| *Top row* | Jersey Milk Can, Bournemouth Ancient Bronze Mace Head, Bartlow Ewer, Winchester Jack, Irish Mather, Exeter Flemish Goblet. |
| *Second row* | Guildford Roman Vase, Felixstowe Roman Ewer, Twickenham Antique Pope's Pipe, Canterbury Leather Bottle, Glastonbury (Abbot Beere's) Jack, Arundel Roman Ewer, Lichfield Jug. |
| *Third row* | St Albans Ancient Cooking Pot, Plymouth Spanish Jug, Peterborough Tripod, Irish Bronze Pot, Cornish Bussa, Ostend Flemish Bottle. |
| *Fourth row* | Boulogne Sedan Chair, Manx Peel Pot, Colchester Oyster Shell, Welsh Hat, Queen Victoria's First Shoe, Hawkins Henley Skull. |

# League and International League of Goss Collectors models

**All dimensions refer to the height unless otherwise stated.**

| Model | | With any Arms £ p | With Matching Arms £ p |
|---|---|---|---|
| **ANCIENT COSTRIL or PILGRIMS BOTTLE** This model was first introduced bearing *THE LEAGUE OF GOSS COLLECTORS* motif (a), and re-introduced later bearing the *INTERNATIONAL LEAGUE OF GOSS COLLECTORS* motif(b). | (a) 56mm (b) 56mm | | 60.00 85.00 |
| **CHESHIRE ROMAN URN** International League Model for 1932. Correct Arms: *INTERNATIONAL LEAGUE OF GOSS COLLECTORS* | 90mm | | 400.00 |
| **CHESTER ROMAN ALTAR** International League Model for 1931. Correct Arms: *INTERNATIONAL LEAGUE OF GOSS COLLECTORS* | 117mm | 150.00 | 800.00 |
| **CIRENCESTER ROMAN EWER** This model was first introduced bearing *THE LEAGUE OF GOSS COLLECTORS* motif (a), and re-introduced in 1918 bearing the *INTERNATIONAL LEAGUE OF GOSS COLLECTORS* motif (b). | (a) 78mm (b) 78mm | | 85.00 120.00 |
| **COLCHESTER ROMAN LAMP** International League Model for 1927 Correct Arms: *INTERNATIONAL LEAGUE OF GOSS COLLECTORS* | Length 100mm Height 75mm | | 185.00 |
| **CONTACT MINE** International League Model for 1919. Correct Arms: *INTERNATIONAL LEAGUE OF GOSS COLLECTORS* (in Gothic script). | Length 73mm | | 220.00 |
| **CYPRUS MYCENAEN VASE** International League Model for 1925 Correct Arms: *INTERNATIONAL LEAGUE OF GOSS COLLECTORS* | Dia. 90mm | | 160.00 |
| **EGYPTIAN LOTUS VASE** International League Model for 1923 Correct Arms: *INTERNATIONAL LEAGUE OF GOSS COLLECTORS* | 80mm | | 185.00 |
| **FIMBER ANCIENT BRITISH CINERARY URN** International League Model for 1928 Correct Arms: *INTERNATIONAL LEAGUE OF GOSS COLLECTORS* | 106mm | | 195.00 |

| Model | | With any Arms £ p | With Matching Arms £ p |
|---|---|---|---|
| **GNOSSUS ASHMOLEAN VASE**<br>International League Model for 1920<br>Correct Arms: *INTERNATIONAL LEAGUE OF GOSS COLLECTORS* | 60mm | | 95.00 |
| **GREEK AMPHORA VASE**<br>International League Model for 1921<br>Correct Arms: *INTERNATIONAL LEAGUE OF GOSS COLLECTORS* | 138mm | | 130.00 |
| **(ANCIENT) IRISH CRUISKEN**<br>International League Model for 1929<br>Correct Arms: *INTERNATIONAL LEAGUE OF GOSS COLLECTORS* | 95mm | | 190.00 |
| **ITALIAN KRATER**<br>International League Model for 1922<br>Correct Arms: *INTERNATIONAL LEAGUE OF GOSS COLLECTORS* | 100mm | | 125.00 |
| **KING'S NEWTON ANGLO-SAXON CINERARY URN**<br>This model was first introduced bearing THE LEAGUE OF GOSS COLLECTORS motif (a), and re-introduced later bearing the INTERNATIONAL LEAGUE OF GOSS COLLECTORS motif (b). | (a) 60mm<br>(b) 60mm | | 80.00<br>95.00 |
| **NORTHWICH SEPULCHURAL URN**<br>International League Model for 1930<br>Correct Arms: *INTERNATIONAL LEAGUE OF GOSS COLLECTORS* | 85mm | | 285.00 |
| **PORTLAND VASE**<br>Correct Arms: *THE LEAGUE OF GOSS COLLECTORS* | 51mm | | 50.00 |
| **STAFFORDSHIRE DRINKING CUP**<br>International League Model for 1926<br>Correct Arms: *INTERNATIONAL LEAGUE OF GOSS COLLECTORS* | 111mm | | 155.00 |
| **STAFFORDSHIRE TYG**<br>This model was first introduced bearing *THE LEAGUE OF GOSS COLLECTORS* motif (a), and re-introduced later bearing the *INTERNATIONAL LEAGUE OF GOSS COLLECTORS* motif(b). | (a) 70mm<br>(b) 70mm | | 95.00<br>110.00 |

| Model | With any Arms £ p | With Matching Arms £ p |
|---|---|---|
| **WILDERSPOOL ROMAN TETINAE**<br>International League Model for 1924<br>Correct Arms: *INTERNATIONAL LEAGUE OF*<br>*GOSS COLLECTORS* | 105mm | 110.00 |

## The League and International League of Goss Collectors Models

| | |
|---|---|
| *Top row*<br>League Models | Portland Vase, Ancient Costril or Pilgrim's Bottle, Staffordshire Tyg, Cirencester Roman Ewer, Kings Newton Anglo-Saxon Cinerary Urn. |
| International<br>League Models | Ancient Costril or Pilgrim's Bottle, Staffordshire Tyg, Kings Newton Anglo-Saxon Cinerary Urn. |
| *Second row* | 1918 Cirencester Roman Ewer, 1919 Contact Mine, 1920 Gnossus Vase, 1921 Greek Amphora Vase, 1922 Italian Krater. |
| *Third row* | 1923 Egyptian Lotus Vase, 1924 Wilderspool Roman Tetinae, 1925 Cyprus Mycenaean Vase, 1926 Staffordshire Drinking Cup, 1927 Colchester Roman Lamp. |
| *Bottom row* | 1928 Fimber Cinerary Urn, 1929 Irish Cruisken, 1930 Northwich Sepulchral Urn, 1931 Chester Roman Altar, 1932 Cheshire Roman Urn. |

# Cottages and Coloured Buildings

**For Glazed Cottages add £20 to stated value.**
**All sizes given refer to the length unless otherwise stated.**

|  |  | £ | p |
|---|---|---|---|
| **(JOHN) BUNYAN'S COTTAGE, ELSTOW**<br>Unglazed | 60mm | 850.00 |  |

**(ROBERT) BURNS' COTTAGE, AYRSHIRE**

| | | | |
|---|---|---|---|
| (a) Small | 62mm | 105.00 |
| (b) Night-light, blue windows with brown glazing bars | 145mm | 160.00 |
| (c) as (b) but with open windows, unglazed only | 145mm | 360.00 |
| (d) Night-light, white, unglazed | 150mm | 215.00 |

**BUXTON, CAT AND FIDDLE INN**   68mm   245.00
Unglazed

**CHRISTCHURCH, OLD COURT HOUSE**   76mm   325.00
Unglazed.

**(CHARLES) DICKENS' HOUSE, GADS HILL,**
**ROCHESTER**   65mm   200.00
There are two varieties of this model - with and without small
windows on either side of the front door. The value is unaffected.
Unglazed.

**FIRST AND LAST HOUSE IN ENGLAND**
Can be found with the badge of Cornwall on one end for which
£20.00 should be added. The small model can be found with either a
green or black door.
This model can be found glazed or unglazed.

| | | | |
|---|---|---|---|
| (a) Small, cream or brown roof, green door | 64mm | 105.00 |
| (b) Small, grey roof, black or green door | 64mm | 115.00 |
| (c) Night-light, cream roof, green door | 117mm | 300.00 |
| (d) Night-light, grey roof, black door | 117mm | 300.00 |
| (e) Night-light, white, green door, brown chimney | 117mm | 335.00 |

**FIRST AND LAST HOUSE IN ENGLAND - WITH ANNEXE**
Unglazed   140mm   850.00
Can be found with the matching arms of *LAND'S END* on
roof for which £50.00 should be added.

**FIRST AND LAST POST OFFICE IN ENGLAND, SENNEN**   73mm   160.00
Unglazed
Sometimes has the badge of Cornwall on one end for which
£20.00 should be added.

**GLASTONBURY ABBEY - THE ABBOT'S KITCHEN**

| Can be found with either black or | Height 88mm | Length 70mm | |
|---|---|---|---|
| brown doors. | (a) Coloured | | 675.00 |
| Unglazed. | (b) White Glazed | | 165.00 |

|  |  | £ | p |
|---|---|---|---|

**GLASTONBURY - CHURCH OF JOSEPH OF ARIMATHŒA**   70mm   800.00
Unglazed

**GOSS OVEN**
There are two varieties: (a) Orange chimney unglazed   75mm   325.00
(b) Brown chimney part-glazed   75mm   325.00
A descriptive leaflet entitled "The Potter's Oven" was issued
with this model and is valued at £25.00

**GRETNA GREEN, OLD TOLL BAR**   125mm   2200.00
Unglazed, sometimes found not marked W.H. Goss,
a factor which does not affect the price.

**GULLANE, THE OLD SMITHY**   75mm   640.00
Unglazed

**(THOMAS) HARDY'S BIRTHPLACE, DORCHESTER**   100mm   375.00
Unglazed

**(ANN) HATHAWAY'S COTTAGE, SHOTTERY**
Glazed or unglazed
(a) Small   64mm   95.00
(b) Night-light   148mm   185.00
(c) Night-light white unglazed only   148mm   265.00
This model was in constant production from the mid-1890's and
minor variations occurred as moulds were replaced.
Such variations do not affect values.

**HOLDEN CHAPEL, HARVARD UNIVERSITY, CAMBRIDGE, MASSACHUSETTS, USA**   137mm   2200.00
Unglazed Night-light.

**HOP KILN, HEADCORN, KENT**   Height   89mm   1575.00
Unglazed

**(DR. SAMUEL) JOHNSON'S HOUSE, LICHFIELD**   Height   75mm   170.00
Glazed or unglazed   Length   47mm

**LEDBURY, THE FEATHERS HOTEL**   114mm   935.00
Unglazed.

**LEDBURY, OLD MARKET HOUSE**   68mm   320.00
Unglazed.

**(RT.HON.) LLOYD GEORGE'S EARLY HOME**   62mm   160.00
**Llanystymdwy, Criccieth**
Glazed or unglazed

|  | £ | p |
|---|---|---|

**(RT.HON.) LLOYD GEORGE'S EARLY HOME**     102mm    140.00
**- WITH ANNEXE, Llanystymdwy, Criccieth**
Unglazed

| **MANX COTTAGE** | (a) Small | 62mm | 125.00 |
|---|---|---|---|
| Glazed or unglazed | (b) Night-light | 122mm | 170.00 |

**MASSACHUSETT'S HALL, HARVARD UNIVERSITY,**
**CAMBRIDGE, USA**         175mm   5275.00
The only varieties known to exist are white glazed night-lights and
bear the Blackpool arms.
Found with the Goshawk mark and inscription in blue.

**NEWQUAY, HUER'S HOUSE**
Glazed or unglazed          (a) Grey      70mm   170.00
                             (b) White     70mm   105.00

| **NEWQUAY, LOOK-OUT HOUSE** | (a) 4 windows | Height | 65mm | 125.00 |
|---|---|---|---|---|
| Glazed only | (b) 5 windows | Height | 65mm | 125.00 |

**OLD MAIDS' COTTAGE, LEE**         73mm    145.00
Glazed or unglazed

**OLD THATCHED COTTAGE, POOLE**      68mm    565.00
Unglazed

**PORTMAN LODGE, BOURNEMOUTH**
Unglazed           (a) With no door    Length 84mm x 72mm    350.00
Unglazed.          (b) With closed door                    450.00

**PRIEST'S HOUSE, PRESTBURY**     Height   71mm   1100.00
Unglazed                           Length   90mm

**PRINCE LLEWELYN'S HOUSE, BEDDGELERT**   63mm    180.00
Glazed or unglazed

**ST. CATHERINE'S CHAPEL, ABBOTSBURY**    87mm    485.00
Unglazed

**ST. NICHOLAS CHAPEL, LANTERN HILL,**
**ILFRACOMBE**
Glazed or unglazed                    74mm    170.00

**ST. NICHOLAS CHAPEL, ST. IVES**
         (a) White, glazed         55mm    170.00
         (b) Coloured, glazed or unglazed   55mm    220.00

£ p

### SHAKESPEARE'S HOUSE, STRATFORD-ON-AVON
Many variations in size may be found, both glazed and unglazed.

| | | | |
|---|---|---|---|
| (a) | Small. Full-length | 65mm | 100.00 |
| (b) | Small. Full-length | 78mm | 90.00 |
| (c) | Medium. Full-length | 110mm | 95.00 |
| (d) | Medium. Full-length | 140mm | 105.00 |
| (e) | Night-light. Full-length. Coloured | 185mm | 180.00 |
| (f) | Night-light. Full length. White unglazed | 185mm | 215.00 |
| (g) | Small. Half-length open door. | 70mm | 115.00 |
| (h) | Small. Half-length closed door. | 70mm | 140.00 |
| (i) | Large. Half-length closed door | 83mm | 140.00 |
| (j) | Night-light. Half-length. Separate base. Coloured | 105mm | 160.00 |
| (k) | Night-light, Half-length. Separate base. White unglazed | 105mm | 110.00 |
| (l) | Night-light, two piece, First Period impressed mark only | . | |
| | so obviously a trial piece [1] | 115mm | 150.00 |
| (m) | Night-light, half length, separate base, coloured (no | | |
| | threshold at base of door opening) | 122mm | 220.00 |

### SOUTHAMPTON TUDOR HOUSE
Unglazed

83mm 350.00

### SULGRAVE MANOR, NORTHAMPTONSHIRE
Overall length    125mm    1100.00

There are many restored and few perfect examples of this model,
which means that sub-standard models are worth less than half of
the perfect price.
Unglazed.

### (MISS ELLEN) TERRY'S FARM, TENTERDEN, KENT.
70mm    335.00

This cottage is unglazed with a glazed, brown roof.

### (ISAAC) WALTON'S COTTAGE (BIRTHPLACE), SHALLOWFORD

| | | | |
|---|---|---|---|
| There are two sizes of this model, but the variations | (a) length | 86mm | 500.00 |
| in size are minimal. The larger size is numbered 834. | (b) length | 95mm | 700.00 |

Unglazed

### A WINDOW IN THRUMS

| | | | |
|---|---|---|---|
| | (a) Small | 60mm | 155.00 |
| Both varieties found glazed and unglazed. | (b) Night-light | 130mm | 300.00 |

### (WILLIAM) WORDSWORTH'S BIRTHPLACE, COCKERMOUTH
Unglazed

81mm    235.00

### (WILLIAM) WORDSWORTH'S HOME, DOVE COTTAGE, GRASMERE
Overall length    102mm    425.00

Unglazed

## THE MORE COMMON COTTAGES

| | |
|---|---|
| *Top row* | Lloyd George's Early Home With Annexe, Lloyd George's Early Home Without Annexe, Old Maids Cottage at Lee Devon, Wordsworth's Birthplace Cockermouth, Cat and Fiddle Inn, Buxton. |
| *Second row*<br>The<br>Cornish Cottages | St. Nicholas Chapel St. Ives, Huers House Newquay, First & Last House Lands End, First & Last Post Office Sennen, Look-Out House, Newquay, St. Nicholas Chapel Ilfracombe. |
| *Third row* | Shakespeare's House Half Length Small, Ann Hathaways Cottage, Shakespeare's House Full Length, Small, Shakespeare's House Full Length (third period), Dr. Johnson's House Lichfield. |
| *Fourth row* | The Old Courthouse Christchurch, Manx Cottage, Prince Llewellyn's House Beddgelert, Burn's Cottage Ayr, A Window in Thrums Cottage, Charles Dicken's House, Gad's Hill. |

# THE RARER COTTAGES

| Top row | Sulgrave Manor, First and Last House With Annexe, Ledbury Market House, Gullane Smithy. |
| --- | --- |
| *Second row* | Goss Oven, Southampton Tudor House, Ellen Terry's Farm, Feathers Hotel Ledbury, John Knox's House. |
| *Third row* | Isaac Walton's Birthplace, Portman Lodge, Joseph of Arimathoea's Church, Old Thatched Cottage Poole, Thomas Hardy's Birthplace. |
| *Bottom row* | Abbots Kitchen Glastonbury, Old Toll Bar Gretna Green, St. Catherines Chapel Abbotsbury, John Bunyan's Cottage, Wordsworth's Dove Cottage. |

# THE NIGHTLIGHTS

| | |
|---|---|
| *Top row* | A Window in Thrums, Holden Chapel Harvard University, First & Last House. |
| *Second row* | Burns Cottage (with Windows), Shakespeare's House, Half Length (separate base), Burns Cottage (without Windows). |
| *Bottom row* | Shakespeare's House, Manx Cottage, Ann Hathaway's Cottage. |

# Crosses

All crosses are uncrested with the exception of the Richmond Market Place Cross.
All dimensions refer to the height unless otherwise stated.
Where no price is given, no piece exists in that particular category.

| Model | | | With any Arms £ p | With Matching Arms £ p |
|---|---|---|---|---|
| **BAKEWELL ANCIENT CROSS** | | | | |
| | (a) White glazed | 145mm | 190.00 | |
| | (b) Brown | 145mm | 255.00 | |
| **BUXTON, OLD MARKET CROSS** | | Grey 88mm | 1750.00 | |
| **CAMPBELTOWN ANCIENT CROSS** | | Brown 152mm | 900.00 | |
| **CAREW ANCIENT CROSS** | | | | |
| | (a) White unglazed | 150mm | 125.00 | |
| | (b) Brown | 150mm | 150.00 | |
| | (c) White glazed | 216mm | 165.00 | |
| | (d) Brown | 216mm | 255.00 | |
| **EYAM ANCIENT CROSS** | | | | |
| | (a) White glazed | 168mm | 155.00 | |
| | (b) White unglazed | 168mm | 185.00 | |
| | (c) Brown | 168mm | 300.00 | |
| **INVERARY - ANCIENT CROSS OF THE NOBLES** | | | | |
| | | Brown 145mm | 1100.00 | |
| **KIRK BRADDAN CROSS** | | | | |
| | (a) Brown | 84mm | 90.00 | |
| | (b) White unglazed | 84mm | 185.00 | |
| | (c) White glazed (Blackpool arms) | 84mm | 47.50 | |
| **LLANDAFF ANCIENT CROSS** | | | | |
| | (a) White unglazed | 147mm | 285.00 | |
| | (b) Brown | 147mm | 565.00 | |
| **RICHMOND MARKET PLACE CROSS** | | | | |
| | (a) White glazed | 130mm | 60.00 | 95.00 |
| | (b) Brown | 130mm | 325.00 | |
| Matching Arms: *RICHMOND (YORKS)* | | | | |
| **ST. BURYAN ANCIENT CROSS** | | | | |
| | (a) White glazed | 43mm | 75.00 | |
| | (b) White unglazed | 43mm | 95.00 | |
| | (c) Brown | 43mm | 225.00 | |

| Model | | | With any Arms £ p | With Matching Arms £ p |
|---|---|---|---|---|

### ST. COLUMB MAJOR ANCIENT CROSS

| | | | | |
|---|---|---|---|---|
| (a) White glazed | 90mm | 75.00 | | |
| (b) White unglazed | 90mm | 85.00 | | |
| (c) Brown | 90mm | 195.00 | | |

Versions (a) and (b) can be found with the Blackpool
arms which would halve their values.

### ST. IVES ANCIENT CROSS

| | | | | |
|---|---|---|---|---|
| (a) White glazed | 140mm | 285.00 | | |
| (b) White unglazed | 140mm | 190.00 | | |
| (c) Brown | 140mm | 295.00 | | |
| (d) White | 204mm | 220.00 | | |
| (e) Brown | 204mm | 330.00 | | |

### ST. MARTIN'S CROSS, IONA

| | | | | |
|---|---|---|---|---|
| (a) White glazed, flat back | 142mm | 125.00 | | |
| (b) Brown, detailed back | 142mm | 200.00 | | |
| (c) White glazed, flat back | 216mm | 185.00 | | |
| (d) White unglazed | 216mm | 185.00 | | |
| (e) Brown, detailed back | 216mm | 250.00 | | |

### SANDBACH CROSSES

This model is made in three sections being held in place
by cork plugs.

| | | | | |
|---|---|---|---|---|
| (a) White unglazed | 260mm | 1300.00 | | |
| (b) Brown | 260mm | 1500.00 | | |

## CROSSES

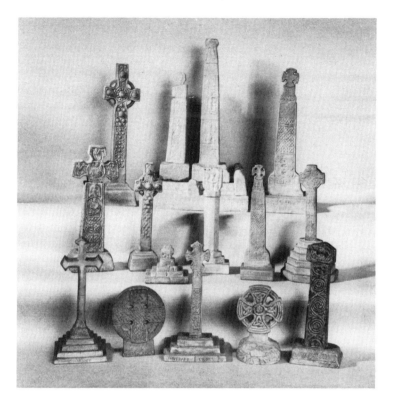

| | |
|---|---|
| *Top row* | St. Martins Iona 216mm., Sandbach Crosses, Carew 216mm. |
| *Middle row* | Eyam, St. Martins Iona 142mm., St. Buryan, St. Ives, Carew 152mm., Campbeltown. |
| *Bottom row* | Llandaff, Kirk Braddan, Inverary, St. Columb Major, Bakewell. |

# Fonts

Models which bear no arms are included in the first column and are marked thus †.
Models from the first period are marked thus [1].
Models from the third period are marked thus [3].
All dimensions refer to the height unless otherwise stated.
Where no price is given, no piece exists in that particular category.

| Model | | | With any Arms £ p | With Matching Arms £ p |
|---|---|---|---|---|
| **AVEBURY ANCIENT SAXON FONT (CALNE)** | | | | |
| | (a) White glazed | 86mm | 115.00 | 175.00 |
| | (b) Brown† | 86mm | 350.00 | |
| Matching Arms: *CALNE* | | | | |
| | | | | |
| **BUCKLAND MONACHORUM FONT** | | | | |
| | (a) White glazed | 75mm | 525.00 | |
| | (b) White glazed (Blackpool arms) | 75mm | 435.00 | |
| Matching Arms: *BUCKLAND ABBEY, NR. YELVERTON* | | | | |
| | | | | |
| **HADDON HALL NORMAN FONT** [1] | | | | |
| | (a) White glazed | 92mm | 75.00 | 95.00 |
| | (b) Brown† | 92mm | 305.00 | |
| Matching Arms: *BAKEWELL OR DUKE OF RUTLAND*, OR *DOROTHY VERNON* (77966 Design) might be considered appropriate. | | | | |
| | | | | |
| **HEREFORD CATHEDRAL FONT** | | | | |
| | (a) White glazed | 96mm | 150.00 | 175.00 |
| | (b) White unglazed† | 96mm | 300.00 | |
| | (c) Brown | 96mm | 285.00 | 300.00 |
| Matching Arms: *HEREFORD CATHEDRAL* OR *SEE OF HEREFORD A.D. 1275* | | | | |
| | | | | |
| **ST. ILTYD'S CHURCH FONT (LLANTWIT MAJOR)** | | | | |
| | (a) Brown† | 88mm | 550.00 | |
| | (b) White unglazed† | 88mm | 830.00 | |
| | (c) White glazed, Blackpool Arms | 88mm | 300.00 | |
| | (d) White glazed with Matching Arms of *LLANTWIT MAJOR* | 88mm | | 875.00 |
| | | | | |
| **ST. IVES CHURCH ANCIENT FONT** | | | | |
| | (a) White glazed | 88mm | 65.00 | 85.00 |
| | (b) White unglazed† | 88mm | 150.00 | |
| | (c) Brown† | 88mm | 215.00 | |
| Matching Arms: *ST. IVES (CORNWALL)* | | | | |

| Model | | With any Arms £ p | With Matching Arms £ p |
|---|---|---|---|

### ST. MARTIN'S CHURCH FONT, CANTERBURY [1]

There are three varieties of this font: Lidded, dished, and open.

| | | | |
|---|---|---|---|
| (a) lidded, white glazed† | 75mm | 75.00 | |
| (b) lidded, white unglazed† | 75mm | 90.00 | |
| (c) lidded, brown† | 75mm | 150.00 | |
| (d) dished, white glazed | 69mm | 65.00 | 90.00 |
| (e) open, white glazed† | 74mm | 75.00 | |
| (f) open, brown† | 74mm | 150.00 | |

Matching Arms: *CITY OR SEE OF CANTERBURY*

### ST. TUDNO'S CHURCH FONT, LLANDUDNO

| | | | |
|---|---|---|---|
| (a) White glazed | 95mm | 60.00 | 85.00 |
| (b) White unglazed† | 95mm | 175.00 | |
| (c) Brown† | 95mm | 215.00 | |

Matching Arms: *LLANDUDNO*

### SOUTHWELL CATHEDRAL FONT

| | | | |
|---|---|---|---|
| (a) White glazed† | 95mm | 115.00 | |
| (b) White unglazed† | 95mm | 125.00 | |
| (c) Brown | 95mm | 300.00† | 300.00 |

Matching Arms: *SEE OF SOUTHWELL*

### STRATFORD-ON-AVON CHURCH FONT

| | | | |
|---|---|---|---|
| (a) White unglazed | 54mm | 32.00 | 40.00 |
| (b) White glazed and gilded (Blackpool) | 54mm | 20.00 | |
| (c) Brown† | 54mm | 350.00 | |

Matching Arms: *STRATFORD-ON-AVON,*
*SHAKESPEARE'S ARMS OR SHAKESPEARE'S CHURCH*

### WARWICK FONT, TROY HOUSE, MONMOUTH [1]

| | | | |
|---|---|---|---|
| (a) White glazed† | 55mm | 85.00 | |
| (b) White unglazed† | 55mm | 85.00 | |
| (c) White glazed but with coloured shields† | 55mm | 115.00 | |
| (d) Brown† | 55mm | 250.00 | |

### WINCHESTER CATHEDRAL FONT [1]

| | | | |
|---|---|---|---|
| (a) White glazed† | 115mm | 300.00 | |
| (b) White unglazed† | 115mm | 300.00 | |
| (c) Black† | 115mm | 300.00 | |
| (d) White glazed † | 135mm | 350.00 | |
| (e) White unglazed † | 135mm | 350.00 | |
| (f) Black† | 135mm | 350.00 | |

# FONTS

| | |
|---|---|
| *Top row* | Buckland Monachorum Glazed, Southwell Unglazed, St. Tudnos Glazed, Avebury (Calne) Glazed, St. Ives Glazed. |
| *Middle row* | St. Martins (Canterbury) Lidded Glazed, St. Martins (Canterbury) Open Glazed, Winchester font Glazed, St. Martins (Canterbury) Dished Glazed, St. Martins (Canterbury) Lidded Unglazed. |
| *Bottom row* | Haddon Hall Glazed, Monmouth Troy House Glazed, Shakespeare's Unglazed, Hereford Brown Unglazed. |

# Animals and Birds

Models which bear no arms are included in the first column and are marked thus †.
Models from the first period are marked thus [1].
Models from the third period are marked thus [3].
Where no price is given, no piece exists in that particular category.
Most animals are not named or inscribed.

| Model | | | With any Arms £ p | With Matching Arms £ p |
|---|---|---|---|---|
| **AYLESBURY DUCK** | | Length 100mm | 220.00 | 300.00 |
| Matching Arms: *AYLESBURY* | | | | |
| | | | | |
| **BEAR, POLAR** | (a) Glazed | Length 125mm | 450.00 | |
| | (b) Unglazed | | 450.00 | |
| Matching Arms: *B.E.E. WEMBLEY* | | | | |
| | | | | |
| **BULL** | | Length 135mm | 450.00 | 500.00 |
| Matching Arms: *B.E.E. WEMBLEY OR ANY SPANISH ARMS* | | | | |
| | | | | |
| **CALF** | | Length 117mm | 450.00 | 500.00 |
| Matching Arms: *B.E.E. WEMBLEY OR COWES* as this was one of the prominent towns in which this animal was sold. | | | | |
| | | | | |
| **CHESHIRE CAT** | | | | |
| | (a) Glazed | Length 83mm | 160.00 | 215.00 |
| | (b) Unglazed | | 160.00 | |
| | (c) Unglazed on glazed base | | 160.00 | |
| Can be found with red and green colour to eyes and mouth, for which £20.00 should be added, or with a blue bow to neck for which £20.00 should also be added. This cat often has a firing flaw in one or both ears, which reduces the price by around one-third. Matching Arms: *CHESHIRE* | | | | |
| | | | | |
| **COW** | | Length 135mm | 450.00 | 500.00 |
| Matching Arms: *B.E.E. WEMBLEY OR COWES* as this was one of the prominent towns in which this animal was sold. | | | | |
| | | | | |
| **DOG** | | Length 133mm | 475.00 | 495.00 |
| See also Prince Llewellyn's Dog Matching Arms: *B.E.E. WEMBLEY* | | | | |
| | | | | |
| **ELEPHANT WITH HOWDAH** | | | | |
| | (a) White glazed | 155mm[1] | 750.00 | |
| | (b) Some colouring, pink or green blanket | 153mm[1] | 1500.00 | |

| Model | | With any Arms £ p | With Matching Arms £ p |
|---|---|---|---|
| **HIPPOPOTAMUS** Matching Arms: *B.E.E. WEMBLEY* | Length 127mm | 450.00 | 500.00 |
| **KANGAROO** Matching Arms: *B.E.E. WEMBLEY* | Height 94mm | 700.00 | 800.00 |
| **LION, STANDING** Matching Arms: *B.E.E. WEMBLEY* | Length 135mm | 350.00 | 400.00 |

**LION, LUCERNE**

| | Length | | |
|---|---|---|---|
| (a) White glazed and crested (at front or rear, usually Blackpool) | 114mm | 47.50 | 160.00 |
| (b) White glazed with Latin wording | 114mm | 120.00† | |
| (c) White unglazed with Latin wording | 114mm | 110.00 | 175.00 |
| (d) Brown unglazed with Latin wording | 114mm | 285.00† | |

This model should have a spear protruding 7mm out of the centre of the back. Often the spear is broken off level with the lion's back in manufacture and is glazed over. Beasts without the 7mm spear are worth some 50% less than the varieties priced here.
Matching Arms: LUCERNE

**PENGUIN**

| | Length | | |
|---|---|---|---|
| (a) Black trim around base, black feet, coloured beak | 83mm | 375.00 | 475.00 |
| (b) Sandy base, no trim, white feet, black beak | 83mm | 375.00 | 475.00 |
| (c) White base, no trim, black feet | 83mm | 375.00 | 475.00 |
| (d) All white glazed | 83mm | 215.00 | 265.00 |

Matching Arms: *FALKLAND ISLANDS*

| Model | | With any Arms | With Matching Arms |
|---|---|---|---|
| **PRINCE LLEWELLYN'S DOG - GELERT** This is an identical model to the DOG listed above, but coloured. | Length 133mm | 740.00† | |
| **RACEHORSE** Matching Arms: *NEWMARKET* | Length 120mm | 325.00 | 415.00 |
| **RHINOCEROS** Matching Arms: *B.E.E. WEMBLEY* | Length 129mm | 565.00 | 600.00 |
| **SHEEP** On Plinth | Length 147mm | 185.00 | 220.00 |

Possible correct arms would be those of any sheep farming areas, e.g. Tavistock. A First Period variation of the sheep not on a plinth can be found

| Model | | | With any Arms £ p | With Matching Arms £ p |
|---|---|---|---|---|
| **SHETLAND PONY**<br>Matching Arms: *LERWICK* | Length 103mm | | 200.00 | 275.00 |
| **SWAN**<br>Glazed<br>For other variations of this first period swan see<br>*THE CONCISE ENCYCLOPAEDIA AND 1992*<br>*PRICE GUIDE TO GOSS CHINA.* | 135mm[1] | | 165.00 | |
| (a) White | Length 170mm | Height 100mm | 750.00 | |
| (b) Naturally coloured† | Length 170mm | Height 100mm | 1300.00 | |
| **WEMBLEY LION**<br>Made for the British Empire Exhibition 1924<br>Matching Arms: *BRITISH EMPIRE*<br>*EXHIBITION 1924 OR 1925* | Length 100mm | | 130.00 | 200.00 |

## ANIMALS

*Lion Standing   Calf   Sheep   Elephant with Howdah [1]   Swan   Penguin [1]*
*Rhinoceros   Kangeroo.*

| | | | |
|---|---|---|---|
| | | | |
| | | | |
| | | | |
| | | | |
| | | | |
| | | | |
| | | | |
| | | | |
| | | | |
| | | | |
| | | | |
| | | | |
| | | | |
| | | | |
| | | | |
| | | | |
| | | | |
| | | | |
| | | | |
| | | | |
| | | | |

# The Concise Encyclopaedia and Price Guide to Goss China

*Nicholas Pine*

Now in its sixth edition, this latest guide has much fresh information including numerous new pieces, many announced for the first time. A well illustrated domestic section clarifies this area of the factory's wares and improved layout and explanations make this chapter easier to understand and pieces easier to locate.

The dimensions and inscription for every piece are given and the Historic Models and Special Shapes section contains the correct matching arms for each model - all separately priced. The very latest revised prices are given right through the book which is also a complete descriptive listing of every piece of Goss ever produced.

The guide is the standard work on Goss china and is used by collectors, dealers and auctioneers worldwide.

The prices given form the base prices of pieces to which the values for particular arms or decorations should be added.

The work is well illustrated and is superbly bound in hardcover with colour jacket. It is a pair with **The Price Guide to Crested China** and the sequel to **The Price Guide to Arms and Decorations on Goss China** by the same author.

**The major features of the Concise Encyclopaedia and Price Guide to Goss China include:**

- Every chapter revised and updated incorporating thousands of detail amendments to previous editions.
- 1300 illustrations - including both common and rare items.
- Every model illustrated - even the rare Haamoga Amaui from Tonga and the newly discovered Letchworth Roman Cinerary Urn.
- All pieces designated into First, Second and Third periods.
- The original inscription on every piece given.
- Every correct matching arms recorded and priced.

- Dimensions given for each piece and variation.
- Over 2500 pieces listed.
- A complete chapter on factory marks with 40 illustrations encompassing every known mark - with dates.
- An informative history of WH Goss and Goss China and many notes for collectors.
- Additional chapters on Goss Postcards, Goss Cabinets, The Goss Records and The League of Goss Collectors.

215mm x 155mm. 1300+ illustrations. 408 pages. Casebound. £19.95

# The Price Guide to Arms and Decorations on Goss China

*Nicholas Pine*

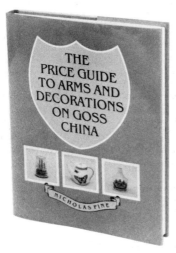

After ten years of research, Nicholas Pine and Editor Norman Pratten have produced a complete listing of all known Goss arms and decorations in a magnificent 320 page, large format Hardback book with full colour jacket.

The book provides a unique and comprehensive listing, with values, of the 10,000 plus coats of arms and decorations which adorned Goss China during its period of production spanning 80 years.

Also included are chapters on the Manufacture and Decoration of Goss China and a History of W H Goss and his factory.

The largest section, geographical place names, now contains 2,200 entries, only *one-third* of the number contained in the first (green cover) book of Arms and Decorations. The majority of those listed in this volume are now known *not* to be Goss First, Second or Third Period, but instead were introduced by Arkinstall & Son (Arcadian) when they took over the works in 1929. All these Arcadian place names, 4,400 in all, are listed in a special section of the new book so that collectors for the first time can ascertain the arms used only by the Goss factory.

The book comprises themes used by the factory including: Chapters on all Civic arms in the British Isles and overseas; Royal, Nobility and Personal; Educational, Medical and Ecclesiastical; Commemoratives and Exhibitions; Transfer Printed Pictorial Views and Enamelled Illustrations; Regimental Badges and Naval Crests; Flora and Fauna; Armour, Flags and Masonic, and late decorations known as Third Period.

The Guide contains over 2,000 illustrations, and every piece listed is priced or valued, sub-divided into over 100 easy-to-use sections.

The book has been designed for use in conjunction with **The Concise Encyclopaedia and Price Guide to Goss China** by the same author. Collectors and dealers who possess a copy of the price guide are strongly advised to acquire this new book so that accurate up-to-date values may be obtained for each piece, for, as often as not, the decoration on a particular piece is worth much more than the piece itself.

260mm x 215mm. 320 pages. 2000 illustrations. £19.95

# William Henry Goss

*The story of the Staffordshire family of Potters
who invented Heraldic Porcelain.*
## Lynda & Nicholas Pine

In this first ever biography of the man who is credited with inventing heraldic porcelain and his family who worked with him and at times against him, the authors tell the story of Goss china in fascinating detail.

From a promising start as a literary student, William Henry Goss used the important contacts he made in London to carve himself a career in the pottery industry in Stoke-on-Trent. At first he produced a limited, expensive range of Parian busts and figurines, but with the entry of his sons, Adolphus and later Victor and Huntley into the business, production switched to the small white models bearing colourful coats of arms for which the firm became famous.

The authors recount the stories of Godfrey, who ran away to New Jersey with a factory paintress, began a pottery there and founded the American branch of the family; the surprising Falkland Islands connection, still continuing today; why William refused to speak to his wife for the last twenty years of his life and how he came to have four homes all at the same time.

The history of the three periods of production is complemented by fascinating chapters on how the porcelain was both manufactured and sold through virtually every town in the country.

The book is illustrated with over 350 photographs and maps, includes much material not previously published and comprehensive family trees.

## As the story unfolds you can discover:

- About the three periods of Goss manufacture and how the trade developed leading eventually to mass popularity nationwide.
- The amazing Falkland Islands connection, how Port Stanley and the Upland Goose Hotel came to be so-named and the exciting story of how the Goss family came to emigrate to those barren islands - and the dreadful fate that befell them.
- Why youngest daughter Florence married a bewiskered Bostonian millionaire older than her father.
- The truth about the rumour that second son Godfrey got a factory girl 'into trouble' and was banished to America. Why did Godfrey emigrate to America? and did he start a US Goss factory?

- The beginnings of William's potting career. Why did he decide to become a potter?
- How the romantic young William became an obstinate and pedantic father and eventually a near recluse.
- Why William did not speak to his wife for the last 20 years of his life - and how he came to have four homes all at the same time.
- His amazing generosity towards his friends and workforce and his unbelievable meanness and cruelty towards his wife and children.
- How William viewed his two sons Adolphus and Victor as rivals.
- Who *really* invented heraldic porcelain and how it was manufactured and marketed.

260mm x 217mm 350 Illustrations 5 Family Trees 256 pages. Bibliography and Glossary.
Casebound. £19.95

# The Price Guide to Crested China
## *Nicholas Pine*

The book, now in its fourth edition, lists, describes and prices every known piece of Crested China. It incorporates the history of every factory, where known, now numbering over 300, and over 500 marks. The author has now incorporated all information originally published in *Crested China* by Sandy Andrews, updated for 1992, resulting in a massive fount of information available in one book for the first time.

Particulars of over 10,000 pieces are given with their dimensions and relevant details where thought to be of interest. The Guide contains a complete listing of all the pieces made by every factory. The history of and all known information about over 300 factories is provided and a mass of other exciting facts answer all the questions that collectors ask such as 'Why does the same piece appear with a different factory mark?' 'Why do some pieces have no crest, factory mark or name?' 'Why are some pieces numbered?'; etc, etc.

In addition to all this information, over 500 line drawings of factory marks are shown to aid identification, the majority of which are not shown in any of the usual books on marks.

The story of Crested China, how the trade expanded and some of the colourful characters involved is also told.

Every item is priced at the current retail price charged by Goss and Crested China Ltd.

The Guide contains a special easy-to-use section of nearly 1000 illustrations, each described and priced, providing a quick reference for the expert, novice and dealer who want a quick visual guide to identification and price.

215mm x 155mm 500 pages. 1000+ illustrations. Casebound. £19.95

*Would you like to join*

# The Goss & Crested China Club

Exclusively for collectors and customers of Goss & Crested China Ltd. Membership will provide answers to question such as:

How do I find the pieces I am looking for?

What is a fair price?

Where can I obtain information on Goss China and Goss collecting?

Where can I exchange or sell pieces I no longer require?

Join the Goss & Crested China Club without delay and receive the following benefits:

**FREE**    Specially designed enamel membership badge.

**FREE**    Membership card and number.

**FREE**    Telephone and postal advice service.

**FREE**    Information on books about heraldic china collecting.

**FREE**    Especially favourable Club members part-exchange rates for pieces surplus to requirements.

**FREE**    Without obligation search-and-offer service for any items and decorations that you seek.

**FREE**    Invitations to Club open days.

**EXCLUSIVE**    Valuation service for your collection

**EXCLUSIVE**    Club Members only special offers announced regularly in Club members monthly catalogue *Goss & Crested China.*

*Membership is free and is available to subscribers to Goss & Crested China* the club's monthly catalogue of pieces for sale.

To join, just send £18.00 annual subscription* to The Goss & Crested China Club, 62 Murray Road, Horndean, Waterlooville, Hampshire PO8 9JL, and you will receive a membership application form with your first copy of the catalogue. Upon receipt of the completed form, you will be sent your enamel badge, membership card and full details of the club's special offers and services.

*For Airmail outside Europe add £12.00

# Goss & Crested China Ltd. are the leading dealers in Heraldic China.

We have been buying and selling for over 20 years and our experienced staff led by Lynda and Nicholas Pine will be able to answer your questions and assist you whether you are a novice or an experienced collector.

A constantly changing attractively priced stock of some 5,000 pieces may be viewed at the Goss & Crested China Centre in Horndean, including Goss cottages, fonts, crosses, shoes, lighthouses, models etc. and the full range of crested ware including military, animals, buildings etc. covering all the other manufacturers.

Visitors are welcome to call during business hours of 9.00 - 5.30 any day except Sunday. Those travelling long distances are advised to telephone in advance so that they may be sure of receiving personal attention upon arrival, but this is not essential.

Most of our business is by mail order and we publish *Goss & Crested China,* a monthly 32 page illustrated catalogue containing hundreds of pieces for sale from every theme and in every price range. The catalogue is available by annual subscription; please refer to the following page for details of this and the Goss and Crested China Club.

In addition, if you specialise, we will be pleased to offer your particular pieces or crests from time to time as suitable items become available. Please let us know your wants as with our ever-changing stock we will probably have something to suit.

Our service is personal and friendly and all orders and correspondence are dealt with by return. You will find us fair and straightforward to deal with, as we really care about crested china and this is reflected in our service.

Finally, we are just as keen to buy as to sell and offers of individual items or whole collections are always welcome. These will be dealt with by return and the very highest offers will be made.

Goss & Crested China Ltd,
62 Murray Road,
Horndean,
Waterlooville
Hampshire
PO8 9JL

Telephone: Horndean (0705) 597440
Facsimile:   Horndean (0705) 591975